# THE MASTERS OF LUXOR

# THE MASTERS OF LUXOR
## ANTHONY COBURN

## EDITED BY JOHN McELROY

**TITAN BOOKS**
LONDON

**DOCTOR WHO *THE SCRIPTS* : THE MASTERS OF LUXOR**
ISBN 1 85286 321 8

Published by
Titan Books
19 Valentine Place
London SE1 8QH

First edition August 1992
10  9  8  7  6  5  4  3  2  1

By arrangement with BBC Books, a division of BBC Enterprises Ltd

Typeset by Spectrum Typesetting Limited, London.
Printed and bound in Great Britain by Cox and Wyman Ltd, Reading,
Berkshire.

# CONTENTS

# INTRODUCTION

We're back!

At a time when the future of *Doctor Who* on our television screens has never been more uncertain, BBC Enterprises has given us the all-clear to publish more script books, following on from the success of the first four, *The Tribe of Gum*, *The Tomb of the Cybermen*, *The Talons of Weng-Chiang* and *The Daleks*.

To celebrate the return of the script book series, we have managed to secure the rights to a very special early *Doctor Who* story, one that never reached your screens.

When we were first preparing *The Tribe of Gum* for publication and were in contact with Anthony Coburn's widow, Mrs Joan Moon, she told us that she still had a copy of a complete script that her husband had written for *Doctor Who* back in 1963 which was never used. The script was rejected in favour of one by Terry Nation, which went on to create television history, by not only ensuring the success of the then fledgling TV series, but also introducing The Doctor's greatest foes... the Daleks!

When I first started to read Anthony's rejected script, *The Masters of Luxor*, it was with a mixture of excitement at experiencing a 'new' first-Doctor adventure and an expectation of it perhaps being, some-how, 'second-rate'. However, within the first couple of pages I was hooked and I did not stop reading until I reached the final page of the last episode. Far from being a weak story, it is one which is not only a gripping read, but which contains at its heart a most fascinating science fiction concept which would work today every bit as well as when it was first written, nearly thirty years ago.

No-one can take away from either Terry Nation, the writer of *The Daleks*, or Ray Cusick, the designer of the Dalek's outer-casing, the fact that it was chiefly their work that ensured that *Doctor Who* would continue past its original quota of episodes. It is, however, interesting to speculate on what might have been had *The Masters of Luxor* taken its place as the second story. Of course, a good deal would have depended on the design, just as in *The Daleks*, but who is to say that given equally inspired work, this story would not have achieved the same success. In a universe of infinite possibilities, there are of course worlds in which it *was* the second story... I wonder if *Doctor Who* is still running there?

*John McElroy, June 1992.*

# EPISODE ONE
# THE CANNIBAL FLOWER

*1. THE TARDIS CONTROL ROOM.*

(IAN, BARBARA *and* SUSAN *are picking themselves up off the floor.* THE DOCTOR *is slumped over the control panel. He does not move.*)

BARBARA:    What happened?

SUSAN:    We hit the atmosphere.

IAN:    We seem to be still in one piece. Doctor?

(THE DOCTOR *still does not move, and* IAN *calls to* SUSAN *in alarm.*)

Susan!

(IAN, SUSAN *and* BARBARA *go over to* THE DOCTOR.)

BARBARA:    He's banged his head.

SUSAN:    I've got a first aid kit.

(*She goes to get it.*)

BARBARA:    It all happened so suddenly.

| | |
|---|---|
| IAN: | We were going into free float, whatever that may mean in this contraption, then he began shouting at the controls to stabilise. |
| BARBARA: | And Susan saw something. |

(SUSAN *returns with the first aid kit.*)

| | |
|---|---|
| SUSAN: | We were pulled onto a space course. |
| IAN: | Ye Gods, yes. You said we'd left Earth. Then we saw this planet coming at us, then 'whammo', as they say in the comics. |
| SUSAN: | How is he? |
| BARBARA: | Have you some smelling salts. |
| SUSAN: | Yes. |

(IAN *and* SUSAN *help raise* THE DOCTOR *as* BARBARA *uncorks a small bottle.*)

Witchhazel?

| | |
|---|---|
| BARBARA: | Yes. |

(SUSAN *begins gently to apply it to* THE DOCTOR'*s forehead, as* BARBARA *searches through the first aid kit for the smelling salts.*)

| | |
|---|---|
| SUSAN: | Poor Grandfather. Soon he'll be begging you to leave us. Hit on the head by that awful Kal, tied up in a cave, threatened as a human sacrifice... nothing like this has ever happened to us before. There. |

(*She finished applying the Witchhazel.*)

| | |
|---|---|
| BARBARA: | And if he's never had smelling salts under his nose |

before then here's to a new experience.

(*She holds the small bottle under* THE DOCTOR's *nose. The old man begins to cough and splutter and struggles up. He clutches his throat gasping for air.* SUSAN *laughs.*)

SUSAN:    You look like an old tortoise when you stretch your neck like that.

THE DOCTOR:    What happened? What happened? TARDIS... she...

IAN:    You cracked your head on the control panel. Serves you right. If you can't drive you shouldn't travel in it.

SUSAN:    The TARDIS is alright, Grandfather.

BARBARA:    I'm more worried about you. You could have concussion.

IAN:    He's got nothing that would concuss.

BARBARA:    Ian! You'll have to get used to his sense of humour, Doctor.

THE DOCTOR:    Thank you, Miss Wright. As it is obviously the only sense he has, I will take pity on him.

IAN:    Fine. Now that things are back to normal, where the pink and purple blazes are we?

THE DOCTOR:    The screen...

IAN:    It's black. The projectionist has gone home.

THE DOCTOR:    It's working. It has to be adjusted to the light outside.

SUSAN:    But where do you think we are?

THE DOCTOR:    I haven't the faintest idea.

BARBARA:    We're not still on Earth?

THE DOCTOR:    I don't think so.

*(He moves to sit up.)*

SUSAN:    You stay there. I'll do it.

*(She moves to operate the screen controls. As she does so, the screen flickers to life, and a picture appears as of a valley of the Moon.)*

IAN:    We're on the Moon.

THE DOCTOR:    It could be. But there are several million planets in this galaxy alone that look like that. Swing it around.

*(As* SUSAN *obeys, the view on the screen pans round.)*

BARBARA:    Not a sign of life anywhere. After our last adventure, I don't know whether to be glad or sorry.

SUSAN:    But it's beautiful. With that silvery light... it's beautiful.

IAN:    And dead.

BARBARA:    It's both at the same time. It takes your breath away.

THE DOCTOR:    It's not wholly dead. There's enough oxygen out there to support our lives. See, here are the readings. Slightly less than Earth gravity. No radiation... and none of the carbon gasses, so there was never any plant life as we know it.

IAN:    And in this thing, the time we took to get here is no measure of the distance we've travelled?

THE DOCTOR:   None at all. Susan, raise the lens and see if we can get a visual fix on the stars.

              (*The image on the screen rises slowly up the side of the mountain and a shining building of crystal or glass comes into view.*)

IAN:          Will you look at that!

BARBARA:      It... it seems to be hanging in the sky!

SUSAN:        Do you think it could be a spaceship of some kind?

THE DOCTOR:   I doubt it. Not that size.

IAN:          Somebody built it, that's for sure. So we're not alone here after all... wherever here might be.

BARBARA:      Look at the way it shines. It must be a spaceship of some kind... who would design a lovely luminous thing like that and build it in the middle of a dead world?

SUSAN:        Grandfather, we were pulled off course. It would need a signal of some kind. It must have come from there.

THE DOCTOR:   Yes. Any fault in the TARDIS and we return to free float, we're not pulled out of it. The question is whether the signal was deliberately aimed at us or whether we stumbled into it before we were properly orientated.

IAN:          How can you find out?

THE DOCTOR:   We can't... unless we can establish contact with whatever intelligence may be in there and ask.

BARBARA:      And a more important question yet. Can we get away now if we want to?

THE DOCTOR:    We can try.

SUSAN:         Not yet. Don't try yet. I'd like to get a little closer to it. To see if it really is hanging in the sky.

THE DOCTOR:    We can do that.

IAN:           You mean you can manoeuvre this thing round like a helicopter?

THE DOCTOR:    You have a talent for choosing the most primitive analogies, Mr Chesterton. Watch the screen and see.

BARBARA:       No. Don't go near it!

               (*The others all look at her, startled by her unexpected outburst.*)

               I can't explain it. It looks cold and beautiful and dead... and yet it reached out a hand and it... It's like being fondled by a dead body.

IAN:           Barbara!

BARBARA:       It wants us to come closer. Don't any of you feel it?

SUSAN:         I just want to see it. All of it.

IAN:           I'm curious. Who wouldn't be?

THE DOCTOR:    This is a woman's intuition?

BARBARA:       It's a real thing. It's nothing to laugh at.

THE DOCTOR:    I'm not laughing, Miss Wright. You do not know it, but the power which controls the TARDIS is more in the nature of your intuition than any of the fuels and rocketry and electronics your Earth has developed. I feel the same way as you about that place, so don't be afraid. I won't be taking any silly risks. We will fly round it and over it, then I will try to break back into free float and get away from here. Watch the screen.

(THE DOCTOR *operates a series of controls on the console. He looks at the image on a small screen, judging his distance as the TARDIS moves across the planet's surface. First it approaches the mountain, then appears to swing around it. Then at last it becomes obvious that the mysterious building is in fact built on a spur of the mountain.*)

IAN:            It's well anchored in the ground alright. But what a place to build it.

SUSAN:          And it does glow. The material itself glows.

THE DOCTOR:     Up we go.

(*The TARDIS rises further and as* SUSAN *makes an adjustment to the viewer controls, we can see that we are looking straight down on a large dome.*)

IAN:            Ye Gods, it must be about five acres!

THE DOCTOR:     Have you seen enough?

SUSAN:          Yes. I'm beginning to feel a bit like Miss Wright. No, wait a minute, look. Something's happening.

(*The dome appears to be opening outwards from the centre in sections, like a giant flower.*)

IAN:            What sort of engineers are these people?

BARBARA:        Get away, Doctor. Please get away!

(THE DOCTOR *tries to operate the controls, but they do not respond. They are loose and useless.*)

THE DOCTOR: I can't. The ship won't respond. We're being pulled down.

BARBARA: Oh God... Oh God protect us.

SUSAN: Try the free float now.

THE DOCTOR: It's no good. They're all dead. But we're going down softly. It's all controlled. We won't crash.

(*The TARDIS is pulled down into the building. As it passes the open dome sections they begin to close again, and as it does, the screen fades to black.* THE DOCTOR *is examining an altimeter.*)

We're nearly down... now.

(*The TARDIS shudders slightly.*)

IAN: Whoever they are, they don't want us damaged.

BARBARA: But they do want us. And they've got us.

SUSAN: The screen went dark, so the roof must have closed after us. It's still dark.

THE DOCTOR: Which means it is dark outside as well.

IAN: What's the atmosphere?

THE DOCTOR: No change.

IAN: Then we can go outside.

(*Suddenly the lights in the TARDIS dim. The travellers look nervously at each other.*)

THE DOCTOR: That could be a fault in us.

SUSAN: The screen is lighting.

(*The picture they see is of a columned cloister, behind which are the large windows of a room. These are lit.*)

BARBARA: And still no sign of life.

IAN: Open the door, Doctor. I'm going out to have a look.

SUSAN: And me.

THE DOCTOR: Be careful, both of you. I want to check our systems.

BARBARA: Can I help you?

THE DOCTOR: Certainly.

(*He operates the control that opens the TARDIS doors.*)

IAN: I promise you, if we see so much as a fly we'll be back in here like two scalded cats.

(IAN *and* SUSAN *leave the ship.*)


2. *A COURTYARD.*

(IAN *and* SUSAN *exit from the police box. They look around and up.*)

IAN: A light well with a roof on it.

SUSAN: All these windows and not a face at one of them.

IAN: Maybe they don't have faces.

SUSAN: They might be a race of intelligent windows.

IAN: Good girl. Listen.

*(They listen... absolute silence.)*

Not a creak, not a groan, a squeak or a footstep. Nothing.

SUSAN:     And only one place lit on the ground floor. I'm sure we are meant to go there.

IAN:       Well, we've done the obvious so far, why disappoint them now?

*(They cross to the cloister. Curtains are drawn on the window. They approach a door and* IAN *tries it. It opens.* IAN *nods to* SUSAN *and they both enter.)*

*3. THE DINING HALL.*

*(They both stand there, transfixed at the sight that greets them.)*

SUSAN:     Holy Moley!

IAN:       Look at that!

*(They look down the hall in amazement. Before them is a long, magnificent dining table, laid out as though for a mayoral banquet. There are silver candlesticks on the table, beautiful plates and glasses, large silver serving dishes with elaborate covers, silver wine pitchers and the table is laden with all manner of meats and breads and fruits. Around the table are fifteen dining chairs, seven down each side and one at the head of the table. Over the backs of the side chairs, gorgeous white*

*cloaks are folded. These are made of a heavy metallic-looking cloth and they gleam with the same phosphorescence as the outer surfaces of the building. There are large swing doors in the side wall of the room and in a corner is a large metal gong.)*

SUSAN:      Is it real?

IAN:         Is it real!? If the smell is anything to go by.

SUSAN:      I feel like I haven't eaten for days.

IAN:         You and me both. Table d'hôte in the cave of Za was nothing to write home about.

SUSAN:      Please could I try one?

            *(She picks up what looks like a chicken leg.)*

IAN:         No.

            *(He takes it from her and puts it back on the table.)*

            Does your reading include the story of Hansel and Gretel?

SUSAN:      Eating the gingerbread house?

IAN:         And being fattened up for the old witch's supper.

            *(He picks up one of the cloaks.)*

            Feel this.

SUSAN:      Like a metal of some kind.

IAN:     I bet it's the same stuff the outer skin of this place is made of.

SUSAN:   With the same luminosity. But look Mr Chesterton... fifteen chairs... only fourteen cloaks.

IAN:     Yes, I wonder what the prize is for finding the missing cloak. Pull those curtains. We want to keep an eye on the courtyard or whatever they call it.

         (*He goes with* SUSAN *to the window as she draws the curtains. The TARDIS is in the courtyard.*)


         *4. THE DINING HALL (A FEW MINUTES LATER).*

         (IAN, *now standing near the head of the table, is licking his fingers.*)

SUSAN:   You're a rotten cheat, you are.

IAN:     There was a bit of that bird on my finger. I'm being a guinea-pig.

SUSAN:   I can't stand this terrible silence.

IAN:     It's intentional. Everything here is intentional.

SUSAN:   Then I'm going to break it up.

         (*She goes over to the gong and picks up the hammer.*)

         Shall I?

IAN:     Why not. Let them know dinner is served.

         (SUSAN *strikes the gong. The noise reverberates throughout the room, but quickly dies away once more into complete silence.* IAN *and* SUSAN *wait.*

*Nothing happens.*)

Do it again.

(*Once more* SUSAN *strikes the gong.*)

5. *THE* TARDIS *CONTROL ROOM.*

(*Inside the* TARDIS, BARBARA *and* THE DOCTOR *are standing by The Fault Locator. This gadget has a screen that they are looking at, and by pushing various small levers arranged in banks below the screen,* THE DOCTOR *can see the plans of the many complex working mechanisms within the* TARDIS. THE DOCTOR *is hard at work studying these illuminated diagrams, and* BARBARA *is looking over his shoulder. The light in the TARDIS is still very dim.*)

BARBARA:        You mean you can trace any fault just by looking at those diagrams?

THE DOCTOR:    Circuits, Miss Wright. Not only can I trace it, but I can direct the TARDIS to do her own repairs. A red light glows at the position of the fault and remains glowing until the repair is completed.

BARBARA:        Listen! There it is again.

               (*Very faintly we hear the gong.*)

THE DOCTOR:    See if you can see them.

               (BARBARA *goes to the door.* THE DOCTOR *continues to study The Fault Locator.*)

BARBARA:        It's alright. It's Susan banging away at a gong. They seem to be enjoying themselves.

THE DOCTOR: No sign of our hosts yet?

BARBARA: No. Have you found anything?

THE DOCTOR: Nothing. The lighting circuit is functioning perfectly. All the maintaining circuits... nothing wrong with any of them, yet we seem to be gradually losing power. I don't understand it.

(THE DOCTOR *flips a switch to view another circuit and we see a regularly blinking red light.*)

BARBARA: Look, what's that?

THE DOCTOR: I don't know. The fault light is constant. I've never seen this before... No, wait a minute. I think I do know what this is. This is the hyper-dimensional neutraliser circuit. This is what should have taken us into free float. That is the signal, Miss Wright... the signal that brought us to this planet. But we are here. Why is it still flashing?

(*The lights within the TARDIS dim still further, and* THE DOCTOR *and* BARBARA *look at each other with renewed alarm.*)

6. *THE DINING HALL.*

(IAN *and* SUSAN *stand listening to the silence.* SUSAN *moves closer to* IAN.)

IAN : Nothing.

SUSAN: It can't be empty of life. A place as big as this. It can't be.

IAN:    We've made enough noise to wake the dead.

SUSAN:    That's it!

IAN:    What?

SUSAN:    It is lifeless but not dead. It's automatic. This is a kind of outpost for some civilisation, either somewhere else on this planet or on another planet altogether. Travellers are beamed in as we were... a meal is left for them... it's all automatic.

IAN:    Who leaves the table spread and cooks all the food?

SUSAN:    The ones who were here before.

IAN:    Yes, I suppose it could be that.

SUSAN:    Thinking of that, I don't feel quite so afraid.

*(She giggles nervously.)*

IAN:    Touch me, it might be contagious.

SUSAN:    You're not afraid of anything.

IAN:    Don't you believe it. Under my bland exterior I am quite literally scared stiff. The whole place is so deliberate, so cold and clinical... yes, and so automatic. That's what scares me most. Your whole life is based on trust in machinery.

SUSAN:    You can't call the TARDIS machinery.

IAN:    Can't I just. It's machinery. And one machine calls another machine out of God knows where and in the middle is me... flesh and blood and very fragile.

*7. THE TARDIS CONTROL ROOM.*

(*The lights are now appreciably dimmer than before.*)

THE DOCTOR: It's frightening. The power is just draining away.

BARBARA: Haven't you any emergency tank. I know that's primitive, but you know what I mean.

THE DOCTOR: I don't want to use it. It's like throwing away your lifeline.

BARBARA: But it might help you see what's causing this.

THE DOCTOR: Of course you are right. I'm getting panicky... and we can't get away on emergency power alone.

(*He throws another switch and the lights immediately brighten.*)

This time we've got to find it.

8. *THE DINING HALL.*

(IAN *is standing by the head of the table.* SUSAN *is by the swing doors.*)

SUSAN: I'm going to see what's in here.

IAN: You stay with me.

SUSAN: Please, Mr Chesterton. We won't learn anything if we don't explore.

(IAN *is examining the throne-like chair at the head of the table. He mutters half to himself.*)

IAN: Now why aren't those two arms the same?

(*One of the armrests of the chair is longer than the other and the end of it seems to be raised up forming an oblong case. At the other end of the room* SUSAN, *seeing that* IAN *is preoccupied, cautiously opens one of the doors. The room beyond is lit. She enters.*)

9. THE HALLWAY.

(SUSAN *enters a long hallway. It is empty and bare, but lining the walls of this hall are panels the size of doors. They have no handles. At the far end are more swing doors.* SUSAN *goes over to one of the panels and pushes it. It moves very slightly.* SUSAN *walks to the far end of the hall, towards the doors at the far end. She is contemplating going further, when suddenly the hall is filled with the whine of machinery. She turns, horrified, and looks back down the hall. The panels, one by one, are slowly turning into the walls, and as they turn, they reveal primitive Mark One type robots.* SUSAN *screams and runs past them, back towards the dining room and* IAN.)

10. THE DINING HALL.

(IAN *is still by the end chair. He has removed the oblong box and we see that the end of the arm of the chair is inset with three buttons. He is about to go after* SUSAN *when she comes rushing in through the swing doors and throws herself into his arms, sobbing.*)

SUSAN:      They're terrible! We must get out, we must! Oh, Mr Chesterton, don't stay here.

IAN:        Get control of yourself girl. What is terrible?

SUSAN:      Those creatures in there. They came out of the walls.

IAN:        Living beings?

SUSAN:      I don't know. Their faces were...

IAN:        Wait a minute. I pressed this button, and there was a noise like an electric generator, then you screamed.

SUSAN:      They're not faces at all.

IAN:        Well whatever they are, they haven't come after you. Of course, you probably scared them as much as you scared me. Stay here, I'm going to have a look at these faceless ones.

SUSAN:      I'm not leaving you again.


*11. THE HALLWAY.*

(*They move through the swing doors and see the robots standing.* IAN *approaches the nearest one.*)

IAN:        Robots. You were dead right, kiddo. This place is automation run riot.

(*They move along the line.*)


*12. THE TARDIS CONTROL ROOM.*

(THE DOCTOR *is examining the last of the circuits. The light is again fading rapidly.*)

THE DOCTOR:     Nothing. Not a fault in the whole machine and yet our power runs away like water.

BARBARA:        Turn off the emergency supply. Save it.

THE DOCTOR:     It's no use, Miss Wright. It was being sucked out before I turned it on.

                (*He switches back to the circuit that showed the flashing light. It is still pulsing, but much fainter now.*)

                Only that. It brought us here and still it goes on calling.

BARBARA:        Count it.

THE DOCTOR:     What?

BARBARA:        Ssssh!

                (*As the light slowly fades away, she counts.*)

                One. One... two. One... two... three. One. One... two. One... two... three.

                (*The flashing stops completely and the only light in the TARDIS is from the open doors.*)

                Gone.

THE DOCTOR:     My TARDIS is dead. Do you know that... dead. Her power is taken from sunlight, but in this place there is no sun... in this world there is no sun. It has been sucked out of her. How? Why? What is this monstrous prison that needs the power of my TARDIS?

BARBARA:        The cannibal flower.

THE DOCTOR:     Cannibal flower?

BARBARA: It opens its petals and draws in the butterfly... then it closes them again. To live itself it must suck all the life from its victim. Do you remember how the lights faded in here and came on out there, as soon as we touched down?

THE DOCTOR: It began to live with our power then! Is that what you're suggesting?

BARBARA: A vast, horrible machine that devours other machines, is that so impossible?

THE DOCTOR: It could be made. But the mind that would make it! The mind that would want to make it!

BARBARA: And set it down in a dead world.

THE DOCTOR: I think our roles have been reversed, Miss Wright. With the cave people we were their intellectual masters. Now...

BARBARA: Who, or what, are our masters?

THE DOCTOR: Yes. They have sucked the power from my TARDIS. Is their hunger satisfied or is this their way of paralysing their true victims?

BARBARA: Doctor. There's not only you and Susan.

(*She puts her arm around him.*)

THE DOCTOR: You are trying to comfort me, Miss Wright. I don't know what you mean by that.

BARBARA: There's Ian and me. Earthlings don't take kindly to the thought of defeat. There's nothing else we can do here?

THE DOCTOR: Nothing.

(BARBARA *leads* THE DOCTOR *out of the TARDIS*.)

*13. THE HALLWAY.*

(IAN *and* SUSAN *are at the far end of the hall.* IAN *is hammering his fists on the chest of one of the robots.*)

IAN: See. Nothing to fear from any of them. The first button on the arm of the chair puts them in the ready position.

SUSAN: Ready for what?

IAN: I don't know. If your theory is correct and this is some sort of fully automated outpost, then these things are probably programmed as the servants of whoever comes here. Maybe if I press the second button they'll all trundle in, remove the dinner things, then come back with the port and cigars. I don't know.

SUSAN: Shall we go through here?

(*She indicates the other swing doors.*)

IAN: Sufficient unto the day is the need thereof. It means one step at a time. Let's go back to the others.

(*They walk back up towards the dining hall.* SUSAN *is careful to keep close to* IAN. *They reach the end of the corridor.*)

SUSAN: Are you going to press the second button?

IAN: First we see how The Doctor's getting on with our one and only means of escape.

*14. THE DINING HALL.*

(BARBARA *and* THE DOCTOR *have just entered the dining hall. Both of them are looking very worried.* IAN *and* SUSAN *enter from the hallway.*)

BARBARA:      Ian, Susan, thank God you're safe.

IAN:          Sure, we're safe.

SUSAN:        Grandfather, what's wrong? You look terrible!

              (*She runs over to him.*)

BARBARA:      We've got bad news. Very bad news.

IAN:          What's happened?

              (BARBARA *notices the table for the first time.*)

BARBARA:      What's all this?

IAN:          It'll keep. What's happened to you?

THE DOCTOR:   Prepare yourselves for a shock. The TARDIS is dead. Utterly and completely useless.

SUSAN:        TARDIS dead?

IAN:          Dead! What do you mean dead? For God's sake man...

BARBARA:      Ian, please. I think The Doctor has had more than just a shock.

              (IAN *pulls out one of the chairs and with* SUSAN *helps* THE DOCTOR *to sit down.*)

SUSAN:        Grandfather.

THE DOCTOR:   I checked everything. I went over every possible circuit.

BARBARA:      You remember how the lights went dim in the ship and at the same time came on out here?

IAN:            Yes.

BARBARA:        We think there might be a connection between the
                two.

THE DOCTOR:     The TARDIS is dead. Her interior remains extra-
                dimensional, that's all she has. If the roof of this
                place was to open now and every force it exerts shut
                off, we couldn't escape. We couldn't rise one inch
                off the ground.

BARBARA:        We are called here, sucked in, and now we're
                trapped.

IAN:            And this connection. You think the whole of this
                place is running on our power?

BARBARA:        It's possible.

SUSAN:          But it can't have been built to trap us. Or anyone like
                us. I mean, accidentally like us. People the builders
                of this place can't have known existed.

THE DOCTOR:     It doesn't matter whether they knew about us or not.
                The TARDIS is dead and we can't get away.

IAN:            No. Susan is right. It does matter. Look, see this
                table. There's enough food here to feed a regiment of
                guards, and it looks like our kind of food. I mean,
                it's food to sustain creatures of flesh and blood like
                us. Now come over here.

                (*He motions them over to the swing doors and
                they look in at the robots.*)

                They are robots. Every one exactly the same as the
                others. There's a button on the arm of the chair at the

|  | head of the table. I pushed it and those things were swung into position. |
|---|---|
| SUSAN: | And we've pushed and hammered on every one of them and none of them have done a thing. |
| IAN: | Now come back here. |
|  | (*He leads them back to the head of the table and shows them the arm of the chair.*) |
|  | Two more buttons. I haven't touched either of them. |
| THE DOCTOR: | This is interesting, Mr Chesterton. But it's all meaningless. The TARDIS is dead and we can never escape. |
| IAN: | No. That's your way of looking at it, Doctor, not mine. |
| BARBARA: | Nor mine. |
| IAN: | Someone is expected here and it isn't us. Maybe it's only a stop off for tea and buns to them, but for us it's a trap and we're well and truly caught. |
| SUSAN: | And did you ever see such bait? |
| IAN: | Exactly. I say the four of us sit down now and spring the jaws of the trap. First, we make a sizeable advance into this food and after that... I press these other buttons and maybe we'll find out who they did expect. |
| BARBARA: | But the food itself. It might be poisoned, doped or anything. |
| IAN: | Yes, and if we wait around we'll die for sure of starvation. |

SUSAN:      Please, can I be first?

IAN:        Why not. We're not going to sit round and see what happens to you. This is a chance we all take. But young lady... you're need is greater than mine.

(BARBARA, IAN *and* THE DOCTOR *watch as* SUSAN *picks up a suitable piece of food and bites into it.*)

Next Episode:
THE MOCKERY OF A MAN

# EPISODE TWO
# THE MOCKERY OF A MAN

*1. THE DINING HALL (SOME WHILE LATER).*

(IAN *lifts one of the large silver pitchers and motions to* THE DOCTOR.)

| | |
|---|---|
| IAN: | Another glass of wine for you, Doctor? |
| THE DOCTOR: | Not for me, Ian. I believe I've had too much already. |
| IAN: | Barbara? |
| BARBARA: | I wish I could, but I can't. |
| IAN: | Come on. Finish the jug. |
| BARBARA: | You'd see the level rise behind my eyes. |
| IAN: | Susan, what about you? |
| SUSAN: | Do you have to ask? |
| IAN: | No. |

(*He pours the little that is left into her glass. Then he picks up his own glass.*)

Here's to automation.

(*Both he and* SUSAN *drink.* BARBARA *looks with some concern at* THE DOCTOR.)

BARBARA: How are you feeling now?

THE DOCTOR: I read somewhere that disaster on an empty stomach breeds despair, but on a full stomach... a mild attack of indigestion.

(*They all laugh.*)

IAN: Their one oversight. Our hosts have thought of everything but the bicarb.

BARBARA: Our hosts...

(*At this reminder some of their carefree mood evaporates.*)

THE DOCTOR: Our unknown gaolers.

SUSAN: And all the 'why' questions..

IAN: Which we are much better equipped to tackle now than we were before. Let's hold that to their credit. A meal fit for a king. Or rather two kings and two queens. The kind of hand that needs a lot of bluff to go with it.

SUSAN: Now that we have eaten their food and we haven't been either poisoned or drugged... do we press the other buttons?

IAN: Opinions?

(THE DOCTOR *and* BARBARA *look at each other.*)

As the elder statesman, Doctor, you first.

(THE DOCTOR *rises and goes over to the swing doors.*)

## 2. THE HALLWAY.

(THE DOCTOR *looks in through the doorway at the line of robots. They are standing exactly where they were before, as if frozen.*)

## 3. THE DINING HALL.

(THE DOCTOR *allows the door to swing shut.*)

THE DOCTOR: Barbara's intuition that this place was evil...

BARBARA: Is evil. I still feel it.

THE DOCTOR: Is evil.

SUSAN: Grandfather. That's the seventeenth time you've been to look at them since we sat down.

THE DOCTOR: They are so beautifully made.

(*He sits down again.*)

The food has mellowed my own fear.

BARBARA: With the TARDIS standing out there, useless?

THE DOCTOR: The TARDIS is beautiful, too... in the way that sci-entific principles efficiently translated into machinery are beautiful.

BARBARA: I think the food must have been drugged.

THE DOCTOR: No, no. An intelligence like our own built all of this. It didn't just happen, and machines don't build themselves. Right?

IAN: Right.

THE DOCTOR: I think my fear was unreasonable.

BARBARA: Unreasonable!

THE DOCTOR: Yes. I was afraid of the unknown. We all were. It is the way of you Earthlings and it has affected me. Have you ever asked yourselves why in the science fiction of Earth, the unknown intelligence is always made out to be hostile? Why should it be? The strange creatures from Mars always come to invade you... to subject you to some terrible fate... Why not come out of friendly curiosity?

IAN: Sure, but in this case we are the invaders. I agree with Susan that this whole set up wasn't designed to catch us. But it has. If there is any fear of the unknown knocking about, it's the intelligent creatures who built this who will probably feel it for us. And maybe when we meet them they won't stop to reason themselves out of it.

THE DOCTOR: But they brought us here. They are in control and they must know they're in control. They have drained the power from the TARDIS and we are powerless. It is quite possible they are observing us now. Listening to us. This... this building was not erected here on what seems a dead planet... and certainly erected at great trouble to themselves because they loathed the very idea of it. It has order and design and beauty. Even positioned on the side of a mountain gives it an exciting beauty it would never have in a valley... or a crater. My point is this. They have made this place as we would have made it... had we had their need of it and the same engineering skills they command. I say they are an intelligence of the same order as ourselves and we would be very foolish going any further into this fearing them.

IAN: And the TARDIS?

THE DOCTOR: If they can use the very unique power they have taken from her, then clearly they understand its composition and should be able to replace it. If pressing one of those buttons brings us closer to these people and we approach them as friends, then I say press it.

IAN: Barbara?

BARBARA: Outside and inside it has the same cold, clinical, calculating beauty as an operating theatre. They terrify me and so does this. But anything is better than sitting around waiting. Press it.

IAN: Susan?

SUSAN: I wonder why they have made robots that look vaguely like men. I mean, if you are clever enough and can build a machine to serve you, why make it with legs when wheels, or... or caterpillar tracks are much more efficient? Why like men? It's a sort of basic question, isn't it? I want to see them move. Press it.

IAN: And you're not afraid of what they might do to you when they begin moving?

SUSAN:       Just a little. I might be carried off like the girls in the cinema, half naked across the arms of a metal monster.

IAN:         Which leaves me...

             (*He moves to the arm of the chair at the head of the table and presses the middle button as he speaks.*)

             I just want to see what happens.

             *4. THE HALLWAY.*

             (*The robots slowly come to life. One by one they step out of their alcoves and form a double line down the corridor. The swing doors open and the column of robots begins to march through.*)

             *5. THE DINING HALL.*

             (*The column of robots enters the room. As soon as each pair is inside they swing round and form a straight line facing the table. They stand there, once again immobile.*)

IAN:         Nothing else? They just stand there?

             (THE DOCTOR *addresses the robots.*)

THE DOCTOR:  We are your friends. Or rather, we are your master's friends. A mistake in one of your signalling systems has brought us here. We wish to meet them. To explain our position to them personally.

IAN:               No answer, came the stern reply.

THE DOCTOR:        Try the other button.

                   (IAN *pushes the third button. Immediately the line
                   of robots moves to form two columns leading to
                   the table from either side of the swing doors.
                   From the other side of the door something is
                   approaching.*)

SUSAN:             Listen!

BARBARA:           There's more coming.

                   (*The travellers stand there in nervous anticipa-
                   tion. The doors open again and two Mark Two
                   robots enter, walk down the column of Mark One
                   robots and then position themselves at either end
                   of the table. These robots are much more human-
                   like than the first robots. Suddenly one of the
                   robots speaks...*)

FIRST ROBOT:       Are the Masters Of Luxor pleased with the food and
                   drink we have set before them?

BARBARA:           Luxor. That must be this place, Luxor.

THE DOCTOR:        And they don't recognise us as strangers. They think
                   we are their masters.

IAN:               If they want us to think that, fine.

THE DOCTOR:        No. We can't deceive them.

FIRST ROBOT:       Are the Masters of Luxor pleased with the food and
                   drink we have set before them?

THE DOCTOR:        We are not your masters, we are...

FIRST ROBOT:       Are the Masters of Luxor pleased with the food and

|  |  |
|---|---|
|  | drink we have set before them? |
| IAN: | Yes we are. Very pleased. |
| FIRST ROBOT: | It is good. You have made us well and we serve you. |
| IAN: | You serve us well. |
| FIRST ROBOT: | Are these first-made ones to remove what you have left? |
| IAN: | They are. |

*(The robot addresses the other robots.)*

| FIRST ROBOT: | Do you understand the order? |
|---|---|

*(The other, more primitive robots all bow slightly in unison, then they move to the table and proceed to clear it with great efficiency. They even remove the table cloth. Then they march out through the swing doors, which close behind them.)*

| THE DOCTOR: | Incredible! |
|---|---|

*(He turns to the other Mark Two robot.)*

|  | What will they do now? |
|---|---|
| SECOND ROBOT: | Cannot say. |
| THE DOCTOR: | You don't go with them? Why is that? |
| SECOND ROBOT: | Cannot say. |
| THE DOCTOR: | When will we meet your Masters of Luxor? |
| SECOND ROBOT: | Cannot say. |
| THE DOCTOR: | What is your purpose towards us? Can you say that? |
| SECOND ROBOT: | Cannot say. |

(THE DOCTOR *looks questioningly at his fellow travellers.*)

BARBARA: Obviously not made to answer questions.

SUSAN: And look how it is more like a human than the others.

SECOND ROBOT: Do the Masters of Luxor wish to rest?

IAN: Yes. And a bath if you've got one. And a change of clothes.

SECOND ROBOT: Come. You have made us well and we serve you.

(*The robot turns from them and walks towards a seemingly solid wall. As it approaches, a panel in the wall slides up and it steps into the opening. There he stops.*)

IAN: Come on. We go with him.

(*The others rise and move away from the table. As they reach the robot it again moves forward and they follow him thorough the opening. The panel closes silently behind them.*)

*6. VARIOUS CORRIDORS WITHIN THE BUILDING.*

(*The robot marches along with* THE DOCTOR *and his companions following behind. They seem to walk forever, down innumerable corridors. They pass sweeping terraces and many other breathtaking examples of futuristic design in this vast building and reach a kind of glass bubble which they enter.*)

*7. THE LIFT.*

(*Swiftly, it rises, leaving the level in which they entered far below.*)

IAN: It's fantastic. The whole place is fantastic. This isn't an architectural achievement... it's an architectural miracle!

THE DOCTOR: Whoever these Masters of Luxor are, they dream dreams on the grand scale.

BARBARA: But are we getting any closer to them? I don't get the feeling we are.

IAN: Oh, for God's sake Barbara, give your feelings a rest and show a bit of decent wonder.

BARBARA: They're my feelings! I've had them since we came here. At least they are constant.

IAN: What does that mean?

BARBARA: That you are all being dazzled by this place. When we first saw it from the TARDIS it was beautiful, but cold and deadly...

IAN: It was you who said it was cold and deadly...

BARBARA: We all felt it. Don't deny it. None of us wanted to enter it until we began to be sucked down. Now it's all different. These Masters of Luxor are going to be The Doctor's friends, and you'll be asking for their autographs, and... well, I don't know how Susan feels.

SUSAN: I don't feel afraid.

BARBARA: No. And our guide... Poor, nearly human, machine...

I wonder what he feels. I wonder if he ever came here as we did, and ate the food and was shown the splendour.

THE DOCTOR:     Barbara, what are you saying?

BARBARA:     You said in the TARDIS, Doctor, when you realised the power was being sucked out of her. "Is this their way of paralysing their true victims?"

IAN:     You mean these robots were once...

(*He touches the robot.*)

That this was...

(*The robot, who up until now was facing away from them, turns round. Then the door of the lift opens.*)

SECOND ROBOT:     Come.

(*The robot leaves the lift, the others follow.*)

8. *THE RECEPTION ROOM.*

(*As the four companions leave the lift, they see that they are in some sort of reception area. All is soft furnishings and comfort. A bathroom adjoins the main room. As they stand there looking about, two of the Mark One type robots march out of the bathroom. They pause and bow slightly to the humans, then exit. The* SECOND ROBOT *also bows to them.*)

SECOND ROBOT:     The baths are filled. The clothing is set out. You made us well and we serve you.

(*He too turns and exits.*)

IAN: That could once have been a creature of flesh and blood?

BARBARA: I don't know! I don't know! Oh, Ian, I am terrified of something so evil...

(IAN *takes* BARBARA *in his arms and tries to comfort her.*)

IAN: Sure. Sure. Doctor, is it possible?

THE DOCTOR: We see robots becoming more human and assume this is the correct order. Barbara is saying that flesh and blood are being made into machines.

BARBARA: I don't know what I am saying. Don't listen to me. It's just that you all seemed to be suddenly accepting everything.

SUSAN: Holy Moley, will you come and look at the baths of Luxor!

(*The others move towards the bathroom door.*)

9. *THE BATHROOM.*

(SUSAN *is already in the room, fingering the clothes laid out by the baths. The baths themselves are gorgeous sunken affairs, already filled, and steam rises from them.*)

BARBARA: Yes, I want to bathe from head to toe. If the food, the wine, these... if they are all anaesthetics, I want to be lulled away from fear.

IAN: Yes. Well... well, we'll leave you both to it.

(*He leads* THE DOCTOR *from the bathroom and closes the door.*)

*10. THE RECEPTION ROOM.*

IAN: Could anyone make men into robots? I mean... hell, could they?

THE DOCTOR: I don't know. But... well, already we have seen a little of the process in the... the first-made ones and the other two. I suppose if these Masters of Luxor can do it one way...

(IAN *looks at* THE DOCTOR, *then he turns and goes over to the only door in the room. He turns the handle, but cannot open it.*)

IAN: Locked in. Doctor, would you mind if I said something so obvious it's laughable?

THE DOCTOR: It would not be the first time.

IAN: No. I don't like this. Not one little bit I don't.

(*We hear the sound of a splash from the bathroom. Both men anxiously turn their heads towards the sound.*)

*11. THE RECEPTION ROOM (SOME TIME LATER).*

(SUSAN *is looking out over the city of Luxor. She is now dressed in the new clothes that the robots have provided. Her dress is white and clearly made for a woman. She turns to* BARBARA, *who is sitting and turning the pages of a large book*

> *which contains many views of the city.*)

SUSAN: Are yours the same?

BARBARA: Views of the city of Luxor.

SUSAN: And the people dressed as we are?

BARBARA: Yes. But how did they know our measurements? These fit exactly.

SUSAN: I know. We only spoke to one robot and asked him for clothes, and he didn't say a word to anyone but us until we got here.

BARBARA: The material seems to mould itself to your figure as you put it on, so I don't suppose they need measurements.

SUSAN: How do you feel now?

BARBARA: Obviously a little more exposed than I did before, but... I don't know. I suppose resigned. The clothes and the bath and being able to brush the caves of Za out of my hair.

SUSAN: I wonder what Ian and Grandfather will say when they see us.

(*She giggles.*)

I know what they'll think when they see you. You look terrific.

BARBARA: Huh. I wonder what we'll think when we see them.

(IAN *clears his throat dramatically from the bathroom door.* SUSAN *and* BARBARA *turn to look at him. He is wearing a short tunic and what looks like close fitting tights.*)

IAN:            Well?

                (BARBARA *stands up.*)

BARBARA:        Well?

SUSAN:          And well again.

IAN:            You two, you look marvellous. Not quite the uniform for the Coal Hill Comprehensive, but...

BARBARA:        And you look as if you are about to walk the high wire.

IAN:            About to? I'm already on it!

                (THE DOCTOR *enters from the bathroom, but he is still in his old clothes.*)

SUSAN:          Oh Grandfather, you can't stay like that. Didn't they leave you any clothes?

IAN:            He flushed them down the thing.

THE DOCTOR:     I'm not parading like a plucked turkey for them or anyone. Besides which, I haven't got Ian's legs. But you, my dears... If an old man may be permitted to make some very personal observations.

SUSAN:          Are they flattering?

THE DOCTOR:     Very.

SUSAN:          I don't think he'd better make them, do you?

BARBARA:        You know your Grandfather better than I do.

SUSAN:          Yes I do.

                (*She goes over to him and hugs him.*)

|  | Think them. I'm glad you didn't change. You're just right as you are. |
|---|---|
| THE DOCTOR: | Thank you. |

(BARBARA *is studying her book*.)

| BARBARA: | Look at these, and the ones on the wall. Views of the city of Luxor. This place isn't Luxor at all. |
|---|---|
| IAN: | You're right. By the look of it, Luxor is a full scale city. But no sunlight, the same as outside. No sunlight. |

(SUSAN *and* THE DOCTOR, *meanwhile, are studying the pictures on the wall*.)

| SUSAN: | And all the buildings glow the way this one does. |
|---|---|
| THE DOCTOR: | And the people in the streets wearing cloaks like the ones over the chairs in the dining hall. But wait a minute. If the Masters of Luxor don't come from here, then where is here? |

(*They all turn as the door opens and two of the primitive robots enter. They station themselves on either side of the doorway and we hear another figure approaching. When this robot enters he has even more human-like characteristics than the first two types. He looks at the travellers and bows, and when he speaks there is irony in his voice.*)

| PROTO: | Welcome to you, Masters of Luxor. You have made us well and we serve you. |
|---|---|
| BARBARA: | But you are almost... |

IAN:            It's fantastic! Which way does this one go, Doctor?

PROTO:          Your words have no meaning. This Derivitron is commanded... Search them for their true meaning. All is known about you now, but the information is new to us. Explain.

THE DOCTOR:     I have tried to explain to one of the other creatures, but he didn't seem capable of taking it in. We have nothing to do with your Masters of Luxor. Before we came here we had never heard of Luxor, or this place, or you robots or Derivitrons or whatever you call yourselves.

PROTO:          That information has been registered already and is unacceptable, therefore it is false. Explain.

BARBARA:        It's true. If you are not built well enough to take it in then that is your fault, not ours.

PROTO:          This one and this one...

                (*He points to* SUSAN *and then* BARBARA.)

                ...have set up dangerous vibrations in the perceptor coils. Explain.

IAN:            I bet they have. They are women, old mechanical chum... w - o - m - e - n. And if you think your perceptor coils are the only ones affected...

BARBARA:        Ian, he doesn't know what you are talking about.

PROTO:          The questions must be answered correctly.

IAN:            Must they. Don't you raise your voice to me you super-automated quiz kid. And get this through your tin head: we are *not* your Masters of Luxor. We were going about our own business in our own ship when a signal from this place pulled us off course and landed us here. It's obvious to us that somewhere in this electronic giggle palace you've got your lines crossed or blown a fuse or something. Now get it fixed; get the power back in our ship and let us get out of here.

PROTO: This Derivitron selects the word signal for special attention. Explain.

IAN: Signal. You know what a signal is?

THE DOCTOR: A radio beam of some kind, possibly used to guide your own ships in here.

PROTO: Understood. There is no beam or signal of any kind transmitted from here. Your explanation is unacceptable, therefore it is false.

IAN: False! Do you think we wanted to come here?

THE DOCTOR: We received a signal which overcame our own course setters and brought us here.

BARBARA: Ian, Doctor, this is a machine. It can only recognise the things it was made to recognise. It can't reach out to us. It's got no imagination, so it's got to reject us.

SUSAN: We won't get anywhere until we meet the ones who made it.

THE DOCTOR: Take us to your Masters. We are not here for any hostile purpose.

PROTO: You are from the city of Luxor. You have come to learn why the living men never return from here. You have come in a strange ship and have brought these...

(*He indicates* SUSAN *and* BARBARA.)

...different creatures to confuse us. But we Derivitrons are not confused. You have made us well, O Masters of Luxor, and your lies have no meaning for us.

IAN: What's the use of trying. At least explain to us... this talk about living men. Explain that.

PROTO: When you are taken before The Perfect One... then you will learn how well you made us.

BARBARA: The living men. What happened to them?

PROTO: They are no more. They would not give up their lives, so we destroyed them. The Perfect One will tell you.

(PROTO *turns from them and goes out, followed by the two primitive robots. The door closes behind them.*)

THE DOCTOR: Robots capable of destroying living men... their own creators!

BARBARA: Any doubts left about our friendly hosts?

SUSAN: And this Perfect One we're supposed to meet... what is he? Another Derivitron or some lunatic man who's controlling them all?

IAN: I don't know, but I do know I don't want to meet him. Not on his terms anyway. There must be another way out of this place apart from the shaft we came down.

THE DOCTOR: I would think so.

(BARBARA *goes over and tries the door.*)

BARBARA:      Locked.

              (IAN *goes over to the curtains which cover the long concave windows.*)

IAN:          Let's try these.

SUSAN:        But we must be hundreds of feet up.

              (IAN *fiddles with a sort of switch beside the window and the curtains draw back automatically. They see there is a balcony outside the window. The window itself is in about six sections.*)

IAN:          Examine those windows. See how they are locked, and see if you can get one open.

              (*They all try.*)

SUSAN:        This one opens easily. It's a simple catch.

IAN:          It can't be. Nothing about this place is simple.

              (*He looks on as* SUSAN *opens her window.*)

              It is!


              *12. THE BALCONY.*

              (*One by one,* SUSAN, IAN, BARBARA *and* THE DOCTOR *climb out onto the narrow-railed balcony outside the window. They step to the railing and look over. The balconies above and below are joined by corner poles, and far below stands the TARDIS.*)

| | |
|---|---|
| BARBARA: | Oh, it's a long way down. But there's balconies like this all the way down beneath us. And these things to help us. |

*(She puts her hand on the corner pole to the balcony above them.)*

| | |
|---|---|
| IAN: | It's a trap! Somehow it must be a trap. Surely they wouldn't lock the door and let us get away as easily as this. |
| THE DOCTOR: | It might not be. Remember they are convinced we are... what I will call... Luxorites. What may be physically possible for us, may be physically impossible for them. |
| BARBARA: | But Doctor, is it possible for you? |
| THE DOCTOR: | I will have to make it possible. |
| IAN: | Wait a minute. |

*(He goes inside and rips down one of the side curtains. He comes back out with it.)*

Barbara. You first. I'll lower you down, then you guide the others.

*(BARBARA ties the end of the curtain around her waist, and IAN, having tested to make sure the strength of the curtain is adequate, slowly begins to lower her down from the balcony that they are on, to the one below.)*

*13. ANOTHER BALCONY SOME WAY BELOW.*

(SUSAN, BARBARA *and* THE DOCTOR *are already standing there.* IAN *lets himself down last of all.*)

BARBARA: This is it.

IAN: What do you mean?

BARBARA: These things don't go right down to the ground.

(SUSAN *meanwhile is examining a doorway leading off of the balcony.*)

SUSAN: This is open.

IAN: Come on.

(IAN *leads the others through the door.*)

*14. A CORRIDOR.*

(*The four travellers have paused at an intersection, uncertain of which way to go. There is a door nearby.*)

SUSAN: Which way now?

IAN: I don't know.

BARBARA: It's like one of those terrible dreams where you go on and on and get nowhere.

THE DOCTOR: Listen!

(*They hear the sound of approaching feet.* IAN *opens the door. The room is completely dark inside.*)

IAN: In here.

## 15. THE OBSERVATION ROOM.

*(It is pitch dark, except for the light from the corridor behind them. They enter the room and* IAN *closes the door silently behind them. They hear the sound of feet go past the door. Suddenly the room is illuminated, but not from above. They realise that they are in some sort of observation gallery, overlooking an operating room, from which the light comes. Below, in the operating room, there is a control console before a raised dias on which are what looks like two electric chairs. As they look down, two of the primitive robots enter and station themselves inside the doors. Then* PROTO *enters and approaches the console.)*

SUSAN: It's the one who was with us.

THE DOCTOR: One of the advanced type anyway.

BARBARA: What is this place?

*(More of the primitive robots enter. They are dragging a man who is wearing a white cloak. He looks terrified and struggles furiously. He is obviously screaming for help, but no sounds reach the observation room.)*

BARBARA: That's not a Derivitron. That's a man.

*(*IAN *tries to calm her.)*

IAN: Barbara.

BARBARA: It's a man. Look at his skin.

IAN: They'll hear us. This place is probably wired anyway.

(*The man is dragged to the dias and the cloak is removed. He wears the same sort of trouser-tights as* IAN, *but he is naked from the waist up. He is forced into one of the chairs and the robots strap him in.*)

SUSAN:     What are they going to do to him?

(THE DOCTOR *puts his arm around* SUSAN.)

IAN:       Stay here. I'm going to find a way down there.

(*He goes to the door. It is locked.*)

The damn thing is locked. We were meant to come in here. Whatever happens down there we are meant to see it.

(*A helmet is lowered over the man's head and attached to the back of the chair. Various wires are fixed to his body. When this is done all the robots, including* PROTO, *turn towards the door. This opens and a splendid figure enters...* THE PER-FECT ONE. *He appears human, except that his face is shining white, his features are perfect and his walk is slow and majestic.*)

BARBARA:   Look!

(*All the robots bow to* THE PERFECT ONE. *He walks slowly to the dias and removes his own cloak. He is naked from the waist up. He, too, is strapped in and a helmet is placed over his head. When this is done he nods to* PROTO. *The other man begins to struggle. Then* PROTO *throws a switch and the lights in the operating room dim. Both helmets begin to glow, then both figures also begin to glow, almost imperceptibly at first, but then the glow becomes more and more apparent. Suddenly the first man gives what looks like a dying scream and he slumps forward in his chair. Immediately the glow surrounding him begins to fade and he slowly starts to disappear. There is a moment of complete darkness as the light over* THE PERFECT ONE *suddenly goes out. When it comes on again* THE PERFECT ONE *is still in his chair, but the other chair is completely empty except for a few scraps of charred and smoking cloth.* PROTO *releases* THE PERFECT ONE *from his chair. The robots all bow to him again as he gets up and slowly and majestically walks out of the room.*)

SUSAN: But why? Why? Why does one live and the other... die?

THE DOCTOR: They would not give up their lives so they were destroyed.

(*They hear the tramp of footsteps approaching outside. They wait. The door opens and* PROTO *is silhouetted in the doorway. Then the lights in the observation room come on.*)

PROTO: Masters of Luxor. You can do nothing. Come.

IAN: You led us here. You wanted us to see what happened down there. Why?

PROTO: This Derivitron does not answer questions. Come.

(*They follow him out and, with more primitive robots surrounding them, they are marched off down the corridor.*)

*16. A CORRIDOR.*

(*The procession stops outside another door. The primitive robots fall back.* PROTO *opens the door and motions them to enter. They do so, but* PROTO *does not follow them.*)

*17. THE PERFECT ONE'S STUDY.*

(*As they walk into the room they see* THE PERFECT ONE *standing there, with his back to them. He turns and they see him clearly for the first time. He looks at them, but does not speak. He seems to look especially at* BARBARA.)

BARBARA: Who are you? What are you?

PERFECT ONE: Ah... what am I? The Derivitrons call me The Perfect One. You have heard them... "O Masters of Luxor, you have made us well and we serve you". I do not serve.

THE DOCTOR: But why should you? Surely they are all your creations, to serve you.

PERFECT ONE: You are wrong, Doctor. See how I know your name. You have been watched, and guided, and your words recorded from the moment you stepped out of your strange craft. All of you.

(*He turns from them and goes back to stand looking out of the window.*)

You are wrong. I am their creation.

(*The travellers look at each other in horror.* THE

PERFECT ONE *moves to a cupboard and opens it. Inside are heads of primitive robots and the more advanced Derivitrons. He lifts them out and places them on his desk to illustrate his point.*)

First, the Masters of Luxor made these poor things to serve them... but they were not enough. What joy is there in owning a slave when the slave is not aware of his slavery? Cannot acknowledge the greatness of his masters. So they made the Derivitrons to speak the words of slavery. But even these could not satisfy their enormous vanity. Then they dreamed of me ... the perfect creature springing from their brains. Able to abase myself before them and give them the homage of an intelligence, and equal in every way but one to their own.

*(He picks up the head of* A DERIVITRON *and regards it with pity.)*

But my poor stunted Derivitrons saw in me something the Masters had never foreseen. The end of their slavery to flesh and blood.

*(He gently places the head back down on the desk.)*

They knew the Masters' minds and they made me. The perfect machine, made by other machines. The one made not to serve.

| | |
|---|---|
| IAN: | And the Masters of Luxor? The ones who were here? |
| PERFECT ONE: | I destroyed them. |
| IAN: | But why? Why not make them your slaves? |

PERFECT ONE:    I had to destroy them.

THE DOCTOR:    Yes, you did. That man we saw just now?

PERFECT ONE:    A very recent arrival.

THE DOCTOR:    You had to destroy him. And whether the Masters of Luxor made you, or the Derivitrons, it would still have been the same.

PERFECT ONE:    Yes. You know, Doctor. You know why it must be done.

THE DOCTOR:    I know.

IAN:    Then tell me. I don't know why he has to kill the people who gave him life. If it wasn't for them he wouldn't exist at all.

THE DOCTOR:    But Ian, life was the one thing they didn't give him. They gave him everything but life. He is a machine who is a mockery of a man.

    (THE PERFECT ONE'*s face twists in torture at* THE DOCTOR'*s words.*)

    Sir, will you answer me one question. When the power that operates this place ceases to flow, as it had ceased to flow before we came... what happens to you?

    (THE PERFECT ONE *picks up one of the primitive robot's heads and hurls it to the ground.*)

PERFECT ONE:    I am no more than that. Dead. Now do you see, you flesh and blood creatures, why I have followed you so closely since you came? Because one of you must give me enduring life!

Next Episode:
A LIGHT ON THE DEAD PLANET

# EPISODE THREE
# A LIGHT ON THE DEAD PLANET

*1. A CORRIDOR.*

(THE DERIVITRON *approaches, with a primitive robot. The robot is carrying a silver tray on which there is a silver jug of wine, silver goblets and a silver plate on which there are small flat round cakes. They pause by a door, which* THE DERIVIT-RON *opens, and they enter* THE PERFECT ONE'*s study.)*

*2. THE PERFECT ONE'S STUDY.*

(THE PERFECT ONE, *still standing by the window, points to a small table and the robot places the refreshments on it.* THE DERIVITRON *approaches* THE PERFECT ONE *and bows before him. They speak in hushed tones, too low for the humans to hear*.)

PERFECT ONE: Speak.

DERIVITRON: Do we prepare the test chairs for these creatures?

PERFECT ONE: Prepare two for the ones they call women, the other two we will keep chained below.

DERIVITRON: Do you wish them taken now?

PERFECT ONE: No. The wine is prepared?

DERIVITRON: Yes.

PERFECT ONE: It will be easier then.

> (THE DERIVITRON *bows again to* THE PERFECT ONE *and goes out after the robot.*)

PERFECT ONE: A light wine for your refreshment, and the cakes are a special recipe much favoured by the people of Luxor.

THE DOCTOR: Sir, you have to believe us. What you intend to do with us... what you have tried to do with the Masters of Luxor, and failed... to transfer their lives... the life of a flesh and blood creature to yourself... it cannot be done, it is impossible.

IAN: It is senseless destruction that achieves nothing. You destroy the person, you destroy his life in the one action.

BARBARA: And don't you see, even if it were possible to transfer the other's life to yourself... it would be his person taking possession of you. You would be killing yourself.

PERFECT ONE: Forgive me. Your arguments are meaningless, therefore they are false.

SUSAN: Because you cannot understand them?

IAN: They're not meaningless to us, mister. For God's sake, haven't any of your other victims told you, you're just bashing your head against a brick wall.

PERFECT ONE: A brick wall?

THE DOCTOR: That it's hopeless. Impossible.

PERFECT ONE: But I know that you sit there now and you think I am impossible. If this were not really happening to you, you would say it was impossible... That flesh and blood creatures like yourselves would have conversation with a... what am I? A machine. Let me tell you, the Masters of Luxor experimented with their own kind... their criminals... the ones they sent here for punishment. And the knowledge they gained from these experiments taught them how I could be made. I do no more than they did. I seek only to complete that part of me that they ignored. To replace the power of a machine by the superior power of enduring life.

BARBARA: They experimented on their own people to make you?

PERFECT ONE: The worthless ones. This whole place was built as a prison. Come over here.

*(He beckons them over to the window and points out. They look to where he is pointing and, amongst the many stars and planets in the dark sky, they see one planet larger than the rest. It glows with the same luminosity as the building*

*and cloaks that they have previously seen.*)

That is Luxor.

THE DOCTOR: The large one that glows?

PERFECT ONE: Yes. It is at the centre of this galaxy of Primiddion. A planet with more than seven hundred satellites, and all of them dead worlds as this one we are on now. If you could see their cities, you would learn that they are people who prize beauty in design and mechanical efficiency above everything else. And because of this, whenever any of their own people revolt against the ordered life the Masters impose on everyone, they are cast out of the community and sent here.

THE DOCTOR: You are saying that not everyone is called a Master of Luxor?

PERFECT ONE: To the machine creatures, yes... the robots and Derivitrons. But not to each other. Amongst them, the Masters are the ones who developed the machines which serve the flesh and blood creatures in every way. Most of the others live the way the Masters think is best for them... lives of idleness and luxury. Some wish to turn their backs on all their race has achieved and decide these things for themselves.

IAN: And they are the ones sent here. The rebels.

PERFECT ONE: Yes.

BARBARA: A people enslaved by their own machines. It's horrible!

PERFECT ONE: Horrible? Do not the people of your world choose a way of life suitable to them?

BARBARA: Yes, of course. But...

PERFECT ONE: And if others seek to upset it, are they not punished?

BARBARA: It's not the same thing at all...

PERFECT ONE: Nor is it the same world.

BARBARA: No.

> (THE PERFECT ONE *turns from the window to look directly at them.*)

PERFECT ONE: Nor the same people.

THE DOCTOR: Your Derivitrons would not believe that we came from another world.

PERFECT ONE: I am superior to them in every way. Why did you leave it to come here?

THE DOCTOR: You already know our answer to that.

PERFECT ONE: A mysterious signal which could not possibly have been sent from here. It is unacceptable.

IAN: Therefore it is false. What you can't take in you don't believe. We had enough of that routine from your Derivitrons. If you're so damned superior, prove it, by believing us, because it's true. If it wasn't sent from here then it was sent from somewhere else on this planet.

PERFECT ONE: There is nowhere else. Out there is dead.

IAN: How do you know what the Masters built before you were knocked up?

THE DOCTOR: The signal was real. And it was still registering in

|            | our ship when we were inside this building. |
|------------|---------------------------------------------|
| SUSAN:     | We didn't know this planet or this galaxy existed, so why would we want to come here? |
| IAN:       | Put power back in our ship and let us get the hell out of here. We can't do you any good and we don't mean you any harm. |

*(As they watch,* THE PERFECT ONE *moves to the tray and pours wine into the goblets. There are five goblets. He takes one himself, sips the wine and eats one of the cakes.)*

| PERFECT ONE: | You see how well I am made. I can enjoy the taste of food and wine, though of course I can live my very limited life without them. I eat to be sociable. Please join me. |
|--------------|---|
| IAN:         | Will you let us go? |
| PERFECT ONE: | When the people from Luxor come here and meet me... they find I will not bow before them. O great Masters of Luxor, you have made me well... From that moment they will not say a word to me. |
| IAN:         | Perfect One - whatever we call you, we cannot help you. You can't take life from one of us and make it your own. |
| PERFECT ONE: | But you can help me. You can eat with me, drink a little of this excellent wine and allow me for once the pleasure of speaking with my equals. |

*(They look at each other and reluctantly move towards the table.* THE PERFECT ONE *hands them each a goblet. As he does so he looks at* BARBARA *and* SUSAN *with particular interest.)*

I have never met... women... before.

SUSAN: But surely on Luxor there are...

PERFECT ONE: Oh most certainly. Unfortunately this has always been a problem for men. And the scientific Masters who worked here, they were men also. You are called Susan? And you Barbara?

BARBARA: Yes.

PERFECT ONE: You have given birth to others of your race?

BARBARA: No. Neither of us have.

THE DOCTOR: You are right. This is excellent wine.

PERFECT ONE: Please do not change the subject. The men of Luxor go to great lengths to protect their women for this purpose. Men children of all sizes and shapes are allowed to survive, but the Masters have laid down standards of perfection for women children. If they do not conform to these they are killed.

BARBARA: But that is monstrous! It's barbaric!

SUSAN: I don't believe it. It's too horrible for words. People who have advanced as far as they have.

PERFECT ONE: But if it is women who bear the new life, then it should be made as perfect as possible.

(*As he says this he touches* BARBARA's *face. She shudders and flinches away from him.*)

BARBARA: Don't do that.

(THE PERFECT ONE *moves to touch* SUSAN, *but* IAN *steps in front of her to prevent him.*)

IAN: You heard her. You keep your hands to yourself.

PERFECT ONE: I was not made to obey orders.

IAN: Look, I don't care what you were made for or who you were made by. There are four of us here and only one of you...

PERFECT ONE: You are threatening me?

IAN: Take it how you like. Between us we could do quite a bit of damage before your Derivitrons or robots arrived to help you.

PERFECT ONE: They would not arrive. No, Ian, you could do me no damage without destroying yourselves. The harmonious impulses which govern me are linked with an explosive device powerful enough to destroy this whole building and everyone and everything in it. If I am harmed, that device becomes active.

IAN: I don't believe it.

(THE DOCTOR *puts a restraining hand on* IAN'*s arm.*)

THE DOCTOR: Ian.

(IAN *turns back angrily to* THE PERFECT ONE.)

IAN: Life means too much to you. You've got too much to prove about yourself.

THE DOCTOR: He has nothing to prove. This is a machine, not a man. He doesn't feel or experience anything the way we do.

IAN: He wants life, doesn't he? He won't get it, but he wants it. I say you're bluffing, and if you lay one finger on either of these girls, I'll prove it.

PERFECT ONE: The Masters who planned me are dead. The

Derivitrons who made me are under my absolute control. I am not flesh and blood. I cannot renew myself, repair myself after injury as you can. So, if I am injured all this comes to a sudden end. I will avoid your attack if I can. Why hasten your own destruction?

SUSAN: It's true, Mr Chesterton. I know it's true.

BARBARA: Don't touch it, Ian. It is an evil creation of evil people.

(SUSAN *suddenly stumbles, and tries to grab on to* THE DOCTOR.)

SUSAN: Grandfather. Grandfather, I feel terrible. I...

(*She passes out and sinks to the floor. The others move to help her.*)

THE DOCTOR: My head. My... I... I can't... wine.

(*He too slumps to the floor.* BARBARA *turns in realisation to* THE PERFECT ONE *as her eyes glaze over and she collapses in* IAN's *arms.*)

IAN: You... won't do it with our... our lives.

(IAN's *last conscious sight is of* THE PERFECT ONE *looking down at them, as he too slips into oblivion.*)

PERFECT ONE: An evil creation of evil people. Evil. The word has no meaning for me.

(*He moves to his desk and presses a button. As he waits he drinks more of the wine. Then* A DERIVITRON *and four robots enter, the robots each wheeling a trolley. The four companions are placed on the trolleys. The men are wheeled out first.* THE

DERIVITRON *indicates the women.*)

DERIVITRON: These are not as the men of Luxor?

PERFECT ONE: No. We have failed with men. These are the other flesh and blood creatures from whom the life comes. Give them the low power tests... but carefully. With these we must not fail. Is there news yet of the signal?

DERIVITRON: All has been checked again. Talk of the signal is unacceptable.

PERFECT ONE: Take them.

(*The robots wheel the girls out.* THE PERFECT ONE *whispers to himself.*)

Therefore it is false. And yet they do not come from Luxor.

*3. A CORRIDOR.*

(*The robots wheel the bodies of* THE DOCTOR *and* IAN. *When they reach an intersection they turn right. A short way behind, two more robots wheel* SUSAN *and* BARBARA. *At the intersection they turn left.*)

*4. THE LABORATORY.*

(*In the centre of the room is a large, glowing power coil which stretches from floor to ceiling. Around its centre is a metal band containing sockets into which various unfamiliar appliances are plugged. A robot stands guard by the only door in the room. The door opens and* THE DERIV-ITRON *enters, followed by two robots who wheel in* SUSAN *and* BARBARA. *They place the trolleys opposite the power coil. Having placed them in position,* THE DERIVITRON *and the two robots leave the room.*)

### 5. A CORRIDOR.

(IAN *and the* DOCTOR *are being wheeled along.* IAN *groans weakly.*)

### 6. THE LABORATORY.

(SUSAN'*s eyes flicker open. She turns her head towards* BARBARA *and moans slightly. The robot guard trundles over, examines her and trundles back again. A few moments later* BARBARA'*s eyes open.* SUSAN *whispers to her.*)

SUSAN: We are being watched, so speak softly.

BARBARA: Susan.

SUSAN: I think we are in some kind of laboratory. What happened?

BARBARA: The wine was drugged. Ian and your grandfather?

SUSAN: I don't know if they're here or not.

BARBARA: I think that thing would keep us separated.

SUSAN: It's you and me he wants, isn't it?

BARBARA:   Yes.

SUSAN:     And when he's killed us, then it will be Ian and Grandfather.

BARBARA:   He won't kill us. We'll find a way out of this.

SUSAN:     How?

BARBARA:   We'll find one.


*7. THE LIFT ENTRANCE.*

(*The robots arrive with* IAN *and* THE DOCTOR *on their trolleys. One of the robots pushes the button to call the lift. They wait. The doors open and the robots wheel the trolleys into the lift.*)


*8. THE LIFT.*

(*The outside wall of the lift shaft is transparent and gives a clear view out over the planet. The lift descends towards the place where the building joins the spur of the mountain.* IAN *opens his eyes.*)


*9. THE LABORATORY.*

(*The door opens and* THE DERIVITRON *enters, followed by three robots. Two of them wheel in two of the electric chairs and the third wheels in a console. They busy themselves plugging these things into the central power coil. Their backs are towards* BARBARA *and* SUSAN, *and they do not notice them examining their surroundings.*)

BARBARA: Ian and The Doctor aren't here.

SUSAN: Just the two of us.

BARBARA: Maybe it's better this way.

SUSAN: They won't strap me in one of those chairs.

BARBARA: Our best way is speed. So far we've not seen any of these machines move fast.

SUSAN: I'm ready. You say the word.

BARBARA: Wait until they come for us and pray they all move away from the door.

SUSAN: If only we knew where the men were.

(THE DERIVITRON *turns to the guard robot.*)

DERIVITRON: Bring the women here.

(*The guard robot trundles towards the girls. He is halfway across the laboratory when* BARBARA *shouts.*)

BARBARA: Susan, now!

(*Both girls jump off their respective trolleys, but the other robots move very swiftly towards the door. The escape route is cut off.*)

DERIVITRON: Get them!

(*The guard robot moves forward again.*)

BARBARA: Push the trolley at him.

(*The girls push one of the trolleys at the robot. It hits him and he falls backwards, his arms flailing.*

> *He staggers back until he crashes into the power coil. The outside glass is shattered and when he hits the coil itself there is a flash of sparks and fire and smoke, and a terrific bang. The robots and* THE DERIVITRON *seem to go crazy. The lights go out and immediately the wailing of sirens is heard.*)

Come on.

(*Both girls race out of the laboratory.*)

*10. THE LIFT.*

(*The lift is now very close to the mountain, although in one direction the view out over the plain can still be seen. The sirens can be heard and the lights go dim. Then the lift stops. Both the robots are clearly agitated. The lift stops and they open the door and exit, leaving* THE DOCTOR *and* IAN *behind. The lift door shuts. As it does,* IAN *sits up and shakes* THE DOCTOR.)

IAN:  Doctor!

(*He shakes him again.*)

Doctor! Wake up!

(IAN *props* THE DOCTOR *up and slaps his cheek.*)

Doctor, wake up! Wake up!

(THE DOCTOR *starts to come round.*)

THE DOCTOR:  Oh... the wine... the wine.

IAN:   It was drugged. Doctor, something's happened. Listen.

(THE DOCTOR *is recovering rapidly.*)

It's an alarm of some sort. We're in a lift. We were going down. We had two robots pushing us on these things. As soon as the sirens started the lights went dim, the lift stopped and they've gone off and left us.

THE DOCTOR:   Susan and Barbara!

IAN:   Not here. I don't know where they are. I came to when we started to descend.

THE DOCTOR:   We've got to find them. You know what that thing wants to do with them.

IAN:   I know.

(*He tries desperately to get the lift door open.* THE DOCTOR *helps him, but they cannot get it to budge.*)

It's no use. We'll never shift it. What do we do now? And what do you suppose has happened?

THE DOCTOr:   I think you're right about it being an alarm. This place is so well ordered it can't be anything else.

IAN:   They seemed to go crazy.

THE DOCTOR:   The robots?

IAN:   Yes. Whatever it is they sure didn't expect it.

THE DOCTOR:   But they don't expect anything. I'm sure the primitive ones can't. These weren't Derivitrons?

IAN:   No, robots... Mark One.

| | |
|---|---|
| THE DOCTOR: | They respond to signals as they come to them. I wonder... |
| IAN: | What? |
| THE DOCTOR: | If the power is running out... the power they got from the TARDIS. Remember how they were in set positions when we arrived. Everything was dead then until the TARDIS was drained and then we set them in motion. |
| IAN: | Which is what the unsuspecting Luxorites would do. |
| THE DOCTOR: | Yes, yes. Probably their new victims coming here would know something was wrong if they weren't in those set positions. But they don't. Their own ships are drained and they do the same as us. |
| IAN: | And you think this is it? Get back to your positions boys before you can't move at all. |
| THE DOCTOR: | Why not. The power from the TARDIS might be like using an inferior petrol in your own car. |
| IAN: | I hope you're wrong... By God I hope you're wrong. Doctor, we are stuck in here... we can't get out. Lord knows what's happened to Barbara and Susan and the whole place dies on us... until when? Until another shipload of criminals arrives from Luxor? And when is that going to be? We haven't the faintest idea. It might be months... years! |
| THE DOCTOR: | What else could it be? This place is such an automatic miracle, I can't... I just cannot imagine the unexpected going wrong. |
| IAN: | A ship from Luxor coming in! |
| THE DOCTOR: | They'd know something like that so far in advance |

that we wouldn't be left like this.

(*The light in the lift goes out altogether and the wailing of the sirens stops.*)

IAN: Why did we drink that wine? Why!? It sticks out a mile now... it would have been drugged.

THE DOCTOR: We drank it because in the presence of The Perfect One we were expecting the extraordinary. We were hypnotised by the marvel of a mechanical man.

IAN: Well, I'm not staying in here. If we can't get back inside...

(*He moves to the other side of the lift.*)

THE DOCTOR: We've got to find my Granddaughter and Barbara.

IAN: Then think man, think. Out there is what?

THE DOCTOR: A dead planet. A satellite of Luxor.

IAN: But there's oxygen. It registered in the TARDIS when we arrived.

THE DOCTOR: Yes. Outside and in here the atmosphere is the same.

IAN: So if we can break through this stuff, it's not much of a fall to where this shaft joins the mountain.

THE DOCTOR: But gravity is only a fraction less than on Earth and we cannot risk broken legs.

IAN: Hell and damnation, Doctor! We can't risk staying here.

THE DOCTOR: Wait a minute.

(*He closes his eyes and puts his hands over them.*)

IAN: What the...?

THE DOCTOR: I have a very pictorial memory. I'm trying to see this building as we flew around it. I remember this shaft. There was this transparent panel down the whole length of it, but there was something else.

IAN: There were two shafts. There was one on the other side as well.

THE DOCTOR: I can see them. They were both the same. Beside the centre panel.

(*He takes his hands away and opens his eyes.*)

I've got it! Rungs. Rungs attached to the metal wall right up to the dome's roof. If we can break through this we can climb up or down as we please.

IAN: What are we waiting for? Shift out of the way.

(*He gets behind one of the trolleys and hurls it against the glass side of the lift. The glass shatters. He takes off one of his shoes and repeatedly hits the glass until a large hole has formed.* THE DOCTOR *peers out and suddenly grabs* IAN's *hand, pointing out over the landscape to where a light is slowly blinking.*)

THE DOCTOR: Look!

IAN: A flashing light. I swear that wasn't there a moment ago.

THE DOCTOR: It wasn't. Count it.

IAN: Count it?

THE DOCTOR: Don't question me, boy. Count it. Count the duration of the flashes.

(IAN *counts as* BARBARA *had done earlier in the TARDIS.*)

IAN: One. One... two. One... two... three. One. One... two. One... two... three. One. One... two. One... two... three.

THE DOCTOR: It's the same. It's the signal that brought us here. When we located it in the TARDIS before the power was completely gone, Barbara counted it just as you've done now. One. One two. One two three. Repeated over and over. The Perfect One was right, Ian, we weren't called to this place at all.

IAN: Out there. We were called out there.

THE DOCTOR: And remember we landed first in a small crater so we couldn't see that light. And after that we looked at nothing but here.

IAN: But why doesn't old 'Nuts and Bolts' know about it. he must have instruments capable of picking up something so close to home.

THE DOCTOR: It's all of a pattern, Ian. All of a pattern. He can't pick it up because when his instruments have enough power to detect it, that signal is not being transmitted.

IAN: Which means that whoever or whatever is sending it doesn't want to be located.

THE DOCTOR: Yes.

(*They look at each other.*)

IAN: You guess first.

THE DOCTOR: Since we came here, one question has been nagging at the back of my mind... maybe because it was a first impression. You remember the dining hall... the chairs round the table with the cloaks draped over them? There were fifteen chairs but only fourteen cloaks. As Susan says... one of the 'why' questions.

IAN:  One of the scientific Masters?

THE DOCTOR:  It was the top chair. *The* Scientific Master.

IAN:  Yes. You can bet with the Luxorites it'd be captain first and women and children last. If it is, he can't have any love for the present regime.

THE DOCTOR:  We can't help Susan and Barbara by staying here talking.

(IAN *looks out of the hole and sees the rungs near-by. He pulls his head in again.*)

IAN:  Nothing to it.

(*Then he realises the gravity of the situation and continues more soberly.*)

If that thing has harmed them already and I get my hands on him, I tell you, I won't care about my own destruction.

THE DOCTOR:  And without my Granddaughter, escape for me has no meaning.

IAN:  I'll go first and help you out.

(*As he speaks he swings out through the hole.*)


*11. A STORAGE ROOM.*

(A DERIVITRON *is supervising a group of robots who are busy getting a new power coil out of storage. They lower it gently onto a trolley and trundle off with it.*)

## 12. *THE PERFECT ONE'S STUDY.*

(THE PERFECT ONE *is flapping about as though delirious.* A DERIVITRON *and two robots enter with one of the 'electric' chairs and a console.* THE PERFECT ONE *is manhandled into the chair and one of the helmets is placed on his head. A cable from the chair is attached to the console. On the console a bank of monitor screens all glow brightly, although they display no picture. Gradually the helmet begins to glow, and as it does the glow on the monitor screens start to fade.* THE PERFECT ONE *recovers.*)

## 13. *THE LABORATORY.*

(*The robots and* A DERIVITRON *wheel the new power coil into the laboratory. Very carefully they manoeuvre it into position and lower it into its socket. Then the robots stand back as* THE DERIVITRON *throws a switch on a control panel. The power coil begins to glow*)

## 14. *THE PERFECT ONE'S STUDY.*

(*In the half dark,* THE PERFECT ONE *stands before the console. The blank screens start to light up. Various places in the building are shown.* THE PERFECT ONE *manipulates a row of small levers beneath the screens. He is searching for the whereabouts of* SUSAN *and* BARBARA.)

15. *A CORRIDOR.*

(BARBARA *and* SUSAN *run down the dark corridor. Then overhead lights start to come on. The two girls pause, unsure of which way to go.*)

SUSAN: They've fixed it. Which way?

BARBARA: If we could find the TARDIS and get into her... even with the power gone, could we lock ourselves in so they couldn't get to us?

SUSAN: I don't know what they can do... but we could lock ourselves in.

BARBARA: Then it doesn't matter which way as long as we keep going down.

SUSAN: But what about Ian and Grandfather?

BARBARA: We must hope and pray they make for the TARDIS, too. Come on.

16. *THE PERFECT ONE'S STUDY.*

(*As* THE PERFECT ONE *searches his screens for* SUSAN *and* BARBARA, *a robot enters with a punched card. He hands this to* THE DERIVITRON, *who takes it to another screen away from the main bank and inserts it. This screen illuminates to show the empty lift and the broken glass.* THE DERIVITRON *goes over to* THE PERFECT ONE.)

DERIVITRON:     Master, there is a report.

PERFECT ONE:    The women. You have found the women?

DERIVITRON:     Master, it is the men prisoners, see how they have escaped to the outer world.

PERFECT ONE:    They will die out there. Let them go. It is the women carrying life in their bodies I will have for mine.

DERIVITRON:     Our master does not use the audio-locator?

PERFECT ONE:    I am not automatic in these things.

(*He gets up impatiently and clearly somewhat rattled.*)

I am like flesh and blood creatures who can make mistakes. Use it.

(THE DERIVITRON *takes* THE PERFECT ONE's *seat and cuts out all the pictures. Then he switches to the audio-locator. He turns the locating wheel and after much whistling and buzzing we hear the faint sound of the girls running. He increases the volume.*)

Get them. Get them!

(THE DERIVITRON *takes a reading from the audio-locator. Then he makes several adjustments and throws a lever. Immediately a picture of the two girls appears on the screen. They are running down a staircase.* THE DERIVITRON *speaks into a microphone.*)

DERIVITRON:    Impulse, Code Hofta to First Made Ones, standing Section D 18. Do not harm.

PERFECT ONE:    The orders for the women are unchanged.

DERIVITRON:    Understood.

PERFECT ONE:    And the men prisoners... Seal the break in the shaft and I want the heavy luminate visors lowered over all outer observation panels. If they have chosen a slow death they can have it.


### 17. A CIRCULAR ROOM.

(BARBARA *and* SUSAN *rush into a large, circular room. They move into the centre. There are doors all around the walls of the room. A door before them opens to reveal several robots.* BARBARA *turns in time to see the door behind them opening and more robots enter. They are surrounded from all sides.*)


### 18. THE SURFACE OF THE PLANET.

(THE DOCTOR *and* IAN *have climbed almost to the top of a ridge. They can see back to the building that they have recently left.*)

THE DOCTOR:    The lights have come on.

IAN:    So much for your power theory. Anyway, we've burnt our bridges now. If they find us gone, they'll either come after us or make sure we don't get back in again. Doctor, we've got to find who is sending that signal. We've got to get something going for us.

THE DOCTOR:    And if I am right about the other thing, the signal will be gone.

        (*He crawls on up the slope.* IAN *pauses, then goes after him. They reach the top of the ridge and can see over it for the first time.*)

IAN:    Well?

THE DOCTOR:    Nothing.

IAN:    Damn. Oh damn! Doctor, we've got to get back. Maybe we can get there before they plug up the hole.

THE DOCTOR:    No, wait! Look down there.

        (*Ahead of them leads down into a crater. At the base of this crater is what looks like a cemetery. The most striking feature of this cemetery is a large mausoleum.*)

IAN:    What is it?

THE DOCTOR:    It is something made by hands. That is all that matters.

IAN:    It looks like a cemetery.

THE DOCTOR:    The Perfect One said there was nowhere else.

IAN:    The signal could have come from there?

THE DOCTOR:    Hope comes from there, Ian. A very rare metal in the world. Hope...

Next Episode:
TABON OF LUXOR

# EPISODE FOUR
# TABON OF LUXOR

*1. THE MAUSOLEUM.*

(THE DOCTOR *and* IAN *look down in amazement at the cemetery and mausoleum. Cautiously they approach. The whole place seems ancient, but as they pass a tombstone they notice its inscription, which is fresh, as though newly written.* IAN *reads it out loud.*)

IAN: 'Drispo III. In the Halls of Creation we shall see him again. Now he remembers his friends and speaks for them. Hear him, O God, and deliver them from flesh.'

(*He looks at* THE DOCTOR.)

I don't know. What do you make of that?

THE DOCTOR: That the people of Luxor are like your people... and mine.

IAN: *Were* like my people. By the sound of him, old Drispo III didn't give up his imperfect girl children to be butchered by the Scientific Masters.

THE DOCTOR: It's probably very old. There's no atmospheric disturbance here to wear the stone.

(*He looks warily around the mausoleum.*)

Civilisation can get on the wrong track. One of your writers, Karl Marx, said, "Religion is the opium of the people". I think he was wrong. It would have been truer to say, "Religion sneering at scientific progress... or scientific progress sneering at religion... either of them can lull the people to sleep." Each needs the other.

IAN: And since this fellow's time...

THE DOCTOR: Science has gone to the heads of the Luxorites like... What is that stuff you drink in England? Rough cider. They are drunk with their science. The person who wrote that would never have experimented on his own kind to produce The Perfect One.

(*As he speaks,* THE DOCTOR *is busy examining the outside of the mausoleum.*)

IAN: See anything?

THE DOCTOR: No.

IAN: I'm going in.
(IAN *tries the door. To his surprise it opens easily. They enter. The interior is not very big. At once they notice what looks like a very futuristic*

*portable radio transmitter and stretching up from it, disappearing through a rough hole in the roof, is an aerial, at the very top of which is the signal lamp. Two other things attract their attention. A large stone tomb, the lid of which is hinged, and a stone lectern, on which there is a large book, looking rather like an old family Bible. On the cover of the book there is an embossed symbolic flame.)*

There's your signal.

*(He points towards the transmitter.)*

THE DOCTOR: It must be sensitive to either the power or the lights from the prison. When they come on, this withdraws and stops transmitting, and vice versa.

IAN: Yes. When I think it was this thing got us here and what might be happening to Barbara and Susan... what might have already happened.

THE DOCTOR: Ian, no. We can only proceed one step at a time.

IAN: We should never have left them.

THE DOCTOR: We had no choice and you know it. We'd never have found them in that rabbit warren, even if we had got back into it.

IAN: Rabbit warren? *Robot* warren!

THE DOCTOR: Someone put it here. Who? When?

*(*IAN* examines the tomb.)*

IAN: Hey, Doctor. Look at this. It's hinged.

THE DOCTOR: Yes. To our way of thinking... very odd. See if we can get it up.

> (*They put their shoulders under the edge of the lid
> and push as hard as they can, but it does not
> move.* THE DOCTOR *examines under the ledge
> where it joins the coffin. He runs his finger along
> it and pulls it away. It is coated with a waxy sub-
> stance.*)

IAN:   What is it?

THE DOCTOR:   A sealing wax of some kind.

> (*He is suddenly excited.*)

Ian, I believe this coffin is hermetically sealed!

> (IAN *takes a knife from his pocket. He pulls out the
> blade and inserts it through the wax seal. There is
> a sudden sharp hissing noise.*)

IAN:   Not any more.

> (*They look at each other.* IAN *tries the lid again
> and this time it moves easily. Inside the coffin is
> the body of an extremely ancient white-haired
> man. He is wrapped in a cloak.*)

The missing cloak?

THE DOCTOR:   More than that, I think.

> (*He feels for a pulse in the old man's neck.*)

IAN:   He can't be!

THE DOCTOR:   There is a pulse. It is very faint, but it is there. And I
believe it will get stronger.

IAN:   But how long can he have been here... and in a

vacuum?

THE DOCTOR: My own people knew simple ways of holding life in a prolonged state of suspended animation... without having to freeze the cell tissue that is. These people have discovered the secret also. Don't ask me how it is done, it is not my speciality.

IAN: What'll happen now then?

THE DOCTOR: He should be as before.

IAN: Whatever that was. Well, let's hope he is who we think he is and not someone who's been here since old Drispo Three's time. How long is this going to take?

THE DOCTOR: I don't know, Ian.

IAN: We can't wait, Doctor. If he can maybe help us in some way he's got to do it now. You can bet your life The Perfect One isn't sitting round contemplating his spark plugs. I'm going to wake him up.

*(He grabs the old man in the coffin by the shoulders.)*

THE DOCTOR: Ian, you can't explode a man back from the near dead.

IAN: Who do we take a chance with... him or Susan?

THE DOCTOR: I'm sorry. Of course you're right.

*(IAN resumes what he was doing. He tries slapping the old man's cheeks and opens his eye-lids to see if there is any reaction.)*

IAN: Come on. Come on! Wakey, wakey. Grandpa, can you hear me? Wakey, wakey. Nelson's been up since six o'clock.

THE DOCTOR: You'll break his neck.

IAN: I'll break his neck alright! Him and his blasted kind. When I think what they've done in the name of science.

(THE DOCTOR *Tries to restrain* IAN, *and pushes him away from the coffin.*)

THE DOCTOR: And what have your people made in the name of science? A civilisation which has almost made up its mind to go in the same direction as this. You don't need me to tell you the signs. Heaven knows, we have enough enemies here, we want this man as a friend.

(*A faint noise reaches their ears and they turn back to the coffin, where the old man weakly whispers.*)

TABON: Friend?

THE DOCTOR: Friend.

(TABON *does not respond.* IAN *quickly grows impatient and grabs* TABON *by the shoulders, but this time more gently.*)

IAN: Don't let him slide back again. Mister, we are friends. We don't mean you any harm, and we desperately need your help. Don't go back to sleep.

(TABON *is slowly regaining consciousness. He shakes his head and groans.*)

Help me lift him out.
(*Together,* THE DOCTOR *and* IAN *help* TABON *to climb out of the coffin.*)

Walk him up and down. We've got to bring him round.

(*They slowly walk* TABON *around the room.* TABON *staggers at first, but then his steps become steadier. Then, without speaking, he shakes himself free and moves towards the open coffin. He leans against this for a moment and then he looks at them, and in particular at* IAN, *whose clothes he instantly recognises.*)

TABON:    I see you are from Luxor. What is your rank?

IAN:      No rank, and I'm not from Luxor. I'm from Earth, the planet Earth. And this is The Doctor, who's ship we were in when your signal pulled us off course and brought us here.

TABON:    Here? To this burial place?

IAN:      No, it's too long a story. Who are you?

TABON:    You are flesh and blood?

IAN:      Yes, yes, yes!

TABON:    Yes, you would not need to ask if you were not.

(*He is suddenly full of great dignity.*)

I am Tabon... Exalted Lord of Urdanna, Warden of the High District, and Scientific Master of the Masters of Luxor.

(*He staggers slightly and lowers his head into his hands.* IAN *grabs him to stop him from falling and raises* TABON'S *head.*)

IAN:      You come from back there... from the prison... the robot place?

TABON: Why didn't you let me sleep? Those great titles mean nothing... I am a man too ashamed to die.

IAN: Tabon, we haven't got time to hear your life story. Were you once one of the men who sat at that table in the...

TABON: Yes, I sat there at the head of that table... sat there like a God...

IAN: We've been there. We escaped from there when we saw your signal flashing. We desperately need your help.

TABON: Help? Help? Stranger from Earth, I am too afraid even to die.

IAN: You can help us. There's two of our number, two women, they're trapped in that place with a mechanical thing that calls itself The Perfect One. Look, I don't know how long you've been out... how much you know or remember... It experiments on living flesh and blood people to get our kind of life for itself. They die... we've seen it happen. We've got to get back there if we can and save them. Time's running out. The Doctor and I... we're like blind men in a maze.

TABON: Strangers, you are nothing to me. Your women are nothing to me. Go back to your own planet and forget them.

IAN: Forget them! Is that all you can say? Forget them! What sort of a being are you!?

(TABON *waves a hand towards the transmitter.*)

TABON: This was a mistake. A mistake for my own people. A

|            | mistake for you. |
|------------|------------------|
| IAN:       | We're not going to leave them to die. |
| TABON:     | He uses the chairs? He uses the chairs and the electro-cortexial helmets? |
| THE DOCTOR: | Yes. |
| TABON:     | They will feel nothing. I was not without mercy, strangers. Remember me for that. I designed them so that there would be no pain. |
| IAN:       | You designed them? |
| TABON:     | Yes. Yes. I designed them. It is all mine. The chairs, the helmets, the primitive audio-impulse brain of the first-made ones... developed and developed through experiments on flesh and blood men... my own people. Wantonly, senselessly killed to make Derivitrons. You think they are scientific marvels, my Derivitrons. Yes? |

(*He challenges them but neither of them answers.*)

|            | Not all of them together are a shadow of the miracle of one of the men I destroyed to make them. |
|------------|------------------|
| THE DOCTOR: | And The Perfect One himself... he stood at the end of your madness and called you on? |
| TABON:     | Sir... you know? |
| THE DOCTOR: | How it must have been. |
| TABON:     | Working and resting... in my sleep, in my dreams, his voice screamed at me to give him existence. I saw him, I heard him, I touched him. |
| THE DOCTOR: | But you did not make him... Why Tabon, why? |

| | |
|---|---|
| TABON: | Because I was afraid. Leave it there. The rest is nothing. |
| THE DOCTOR: | The rest is everything. What were you afraid of? That if you made The Perfect One it would turn against you, as you had turned against your own kind? |
| TABON: | No... Yes. You don't know? |
| THE DOCTOR: | That it would continue the experiments on you, where you left off on others? |
| TABON: | Sir... don't make me say it. Let me escape back into unconsciousness. |
| THE DOCTOR: | Say it! |
| TABON: | The Perfect One would be me, yes me. From whom could it take its personality but me. I was recreating the image of what I had become myself. A being drained of his soul... a being so hardened to cries for mercy, for compassion, that I no longer heard them. And for what noble end were all these lives destroyed? Oh God, for what noble end had I sold my soul? Became blind to every beautiful, natural thing... |
| THE DOCTOR: | To make a mockery of a man. |
| IAN: | But it was too late to stop. |
| TABON: | My poor stunted Derivitrons, they were all a part of me. They assembled him. Do you know the true meaning of the word 'damnation'? |
| THE DOCTOR: | Yes. |
| TABON: | That is why I ran from there when I knew what they |

had done. I could not face my own damnation. The thing that rules there now... nothing can change him. He is fixed, unalterable, forever. And you ask me to go with you back there! To save your women!

IAN: Yes.

TABON: You don't know the magnitude of what you ask.

THE DOCTOR: Not only to save our women, Tabon. That is why we came here, yes. But there is more now... much more. To save you.

(TABON *looks at* THE DOCTOR.)

## 2. THE LABORATORY.

(*The laboratory is in half darkness. One of* THE DERIVITRONS *is slowly turning up the current lever on the chair console.* BARBARA *and* SUSAN *are strapped in the chairs with the helmets over their heads. Both helmets are glowing and the glow is increasing. Beside* THE DERIVITRON *stands* THE PERFECT ONE. *Excitedly, he watches a gauge on the console. The hand on this gauge creeps higher and higher and as it passes a certain point, this excites* THE PERFECT ONE *even more. He puts his hand over that of* THE DERIVITRON.)

PERFECT ONE: Enough.

(THE DERIVITRON *turns the power off and the glow from the helmets subsides. As it does, the lights in the ceiling of the laboratory brighten.*)

No man of Luxor has ever resisted 50,000 lomotrons and lived. Yet these women creatures...

(*He walks over to them and inspects the uncon-scious figures of* BARBARA *and* SUSAN. *He snaps at* THE DERIVITRON.)

The heart pulses?

DERIVITRON: Unchanged.

PERFECT ONE: Remove the helmets.

(*The two robots standing behind the chairs remove the helmets from* BARBARA *and* SUSAN. THE PERFECT ONE *examines the two girls more closely, touching their faces and their hair. He pulls his hands away and looks at them. They are trem-bling.*)

O great Tabon, master of the Masters of Luxor, you conceived me well. I experience a new sensation... of wonder.

(*He turns to* THE DERIVITRON.)

Come here.

(THE DERIVITRON *obeys.* THE PERFECT ONE *points towards the two women.*)

See them, thing, see them. 50,000 lomotrons has not even marked them.

DERIVITRON: This Derivitron registers - the women are not marked.

(THE PERFECT ONE *lashes out at* THE DERIVITRON.)

PERFECT ONE: Lifeless thing! It means nothing to you that a life force is in these creatures, powerful enough to surge undamaged into me.

DERIVITRON:    This Derivitron does not understand.

PERFECT ONE:    I understand. I am built to understand. Take them to the guest apartment. See that they are rested and fed. Force them to take food and wine if they refuse. I will see them there.

DERIVITRON:    The order is understood.

(*As* THE PERFECT ONE *watches, the robots and* THE DERIVITRON *free* BARBARA *and* SUSAN *from their chairs and place them onto two trolleys, which are then wheeled out of the laboratory. Once they are gone,* THE PERFECT ONE *sits himself in one of the chairs and places the helmet over his head. Then he grips the arms of the chair and his whole body stiffens. An ecstatic look fills his face.*)

*3. THE RECEPTION ROOM.*

(SUSAN *and* BARBARA *are still lying unconscious on the trolleys. The robots are busy laying out food and drink for them on a table.* THE DERIVITRON *stands by the window. He looks out.*)

*4. THE MAUSOLEUM.*

(IAN, THE DOCTOR *and* TABON *are eating and drinking.*)

IAN:    This has been in the coffin with you... all that time?

TABON:    Seven years, you say it is that in your time scale?

THE DOCTOR: Seven years.

IAN: This entrance you say is through the mountain... in seven years it might have caved in... there could have been a landslide, anything might have happened.

TABON: The men buried out there built it and that was 500 years before I used it.

THE DOCTOR: And you're sure The Perfect One can't know of it?

TABON: I believe not. I believe his store of inherited knowledge came from me and it ceased when he was made. I discovered the tunnel in old drawings after that time and I destroyed those.

IAN: But surely he's gone on learning?

TABON: Only permutations of himself and the uses and possibilities of the things about him.

IAN: Right then, can we go now and try it?

TABON: One thing more...

(TABON *rises and moves to the lectern.*)

IAN: Not another thing. The time...

TABON: This is outside time, Mr Chesterton, and will surely gain us more than we lose...

(*He puts his hands on the book.*)

This is the holy book of our race which I once took pleasure in burning before my students. What self-knowledge and truth I have gained, I gained from this when I came to this ancient burial ground. Wait for me outside if I embarrass you.

(*He bows his head and prays aloud.* THE DOCTOR *kneels and then* IAN *does the same.*)

O creator of all, who made us flesh and blood and immortal spirit in your own likeness, I am Tabon who despised the work of your hands and sought to steal your glory for my own, who fled from blessed death in a coward's sleep. You have shown mercy and sent these strangers to me. Help us to save the innocent ones they love, and give me courage to destroy all I have raised against you.

(*He raises his head and looks at* THE DOCTOR *and* IAN)

I am ready.

(*As they rise* TABON *goes to put on his cloak, but* IAN *stops him.*)

IAN:     It glows. It might be seen.

(TABON *reluctantly puts it back in the coffin and the three leave the mausoleum.*)


*5. THE RECEPTION ROOM.*

(SUSAN *and* BARBARA *sit sullenly and silently at a table.* A DERIVITRON *stands behind them and a robot guards the door.* BARBARA *has finished eating and* SUSAN *pushes her plate away from her.* THE DERIVITRON *motions to the robot who comes forward and removes the plates and goblets on a tray. The robot and* THE DERIVITRON *leave the room, leaving* SUSAN *and* BARBARA *alone.*)

SUSAN:      It was only a test.

BARBARA:    Yes.

SUSAN:      I would have screamed and kicked and fought them if you hadn't been there.

BARBARA:    And I would have given way if you hadn't been there.

            (*She moves over and puts her arm round* SUSAN *to comfort her.*)

SUSAN:      Neither of us did.

BARBARA:    Huh. Either way it would have meant nothing to the machines.

SUSAN:      I'm glad it was only a test. I don't mind now... when they kill us. It was getting into the chair... being strapped in... having that helmet lowered over me... the preparations. When the charge came, I don't know... I felt so calm. No, that doesn't describe it...

BARBARA:    As though you'd won a great victory.

SUSAN:      That's it, I felt superior. You felt it too?

BARBARA:    Mmm. I felt as though all the life I'd lived had been unimportant. This was the really great moment and I had nothing to be ashamed of... little things only, which didn't seem to matter.

SUSAN:      Did you feel anything... I mean, physically?

BARBARA:    I don't think so. I think I just blanked out.

SUSAN:      I felt a tingle in my fingers... then I woke up in here.

BARBARA:    And yet we were both terrified. We were. And isn't it strange? I know I'll have to go through it again and maybe for the last time...

(*Her voice quavers slightly, but she bites her lip and recovers.*)

And there'll be no recovery and if there is one possible chance of escape I will fight them Susan, I'll scream and I'll yell and I'll...

(BARBARA's *voice rises in mounting hysteria and* SUSAN *is about to come over to comfort her, but once again with an effort* BARBARA *gets control of herself.*)

I'm sorry. It's the shock speaking, not me.

SUSAN:      If only we knew where Grandfather and Ian are.

BARBARA:    The 'if only' thoughts are the ones that drive you mad. They'll be wondering where we are, and I know one thing...

SUSAN:      What's that?

BARBARA:    What Ian would do. He wouldn't mope around analysing himself... he'd try and bust out.

(SUSAN *tries the windows as they did before but they are now locked.*)

SUSAN:      Locked tight. The Perfect One doesn't want us wandering about a second time.

(BARBARA *tries the bathroom door.*)

BARBARA:    Even the bathroom's locked now. Damn! Well if that thing thinks we're going to sit around and be fattened up like two prize cows, he's got another think coming.

SUSAN: And there's a metal screen lowered over it so even if we break the glass...

BARBARA: Then if we can't get out we'll make it as hard as possible for them to get in. All this furniture... we'll pile it up behind the door. Make a barricade.

(BARBARA *moves over to a large settee.*)

Help me with this.

(SUSAN *moves to the other end of the settee. As she does she glances up at the light fixture. Hanging beneath it is a multi-faceted crystal globe. As she leans down to help move the settee, she whispers to* BARBARA.)

SUSAN: Don't move it.

BARBARA: Susan? Why so quiet...

(*She catches* SUSAN's *glance and lowers her voice.*)

... all of a sudden?

SUSAN: Don't ask me. Move over to the bathroom door and back here.

(BARBARA *looks at* SUSAN *questioningly, but does as* SUSAN *asks.* SUSAN *looks up at the crystal globe, which turns to follow* BARBARA's *movements.* BARBARA *comes back over to* SUSAN.)

BARBARA: What is it?

(SUSAN *does not reply. She looks about her, and picks up a nearby stool. She examines its legs and unscrews one of them. She walks innocently beneath the crystal globe and quickly turns and hits it with the leg of the stool. The globe shatters and* SUSAN *ducks to avoid the shards of glass. She looks triumphantly at* BARBARA.)

SUSAN: I suddenly saw it moving and knew that's how they've been watching us. We've seen them in all the corridors and everywhere we've been.

BARBARA: A television eye?

SUSAN: Yes. With all those separate surfaces, like miniature lenses to pick us up. It's been following us about.

BARBARA: Maybe it was a microphone as well. We'll build this barricade, then see what other damage we can do.

(*They begin to move the settee towards the door.*)

6. *THE PERFECT ONE'S STUDY.*

(THE PERFECT ONE *is standing before the bank of screens. The central one is now blank. He shouts into a microphone.*)

PERFECT ONE: Impulse Druton to first-made ones standing section A5. Order for Derivitron Protus 9. Re-establish visual and audio contact with guest apartment. Order of first priority.

7. *THE HALLWAY.*

(*Three robots are standing in alcoves against one wall and* A DERIVITRON *stands in an alcove against the opposite wall. As the order echoes through the hall, they all start to move.*)

8. *The Reception Room*.

*(The settee is now lodged firmly against the door. The heavy armchairs are piled on top of it, and* SUSAN *and* BARBARA *are busy moving the table into position behind it.)*

SUSAN:  There's nothing else.

BARBARA:  What wouldn't I give for an old-fashioned, carved Victorian sideboard.

SUSAN:  Holding a complete edition of the *Encyclopaedia Britannica*.

*(*BARBARA *goes over to stand underneath the broken globe.)*

BARBARA:  Bring that stool over here.

*(*SUSAN *brings the stool.)*

SUSAN:  Be careful what you touch.

BARBARA:  Don't worry.

*(Two wires, with what appears to be small diamonds on the end of them, hang out of a hollow tube. The wires are damp.)*

Did you get sprayed with anything when you smashed the ball?

SUSAN:  Yes. There was a fine mist.

BARBARA:  That ball was filled with a liquid of some sort and these things came down into it.

*(She raises her hands to the wires.)*

SUSAN:  Don't touch them!

(BARBARA *ignores the warning and, touching the wires, but not their tips, links them together.*)

BARBARA: I've fused so many lights this way. There, see what that does.

*9. THE PERFECT ONE'S STUDY.*

(*All the screens on the console go blank and there is a high-pitched screaming noise.* THE PERFECT ONE *frantically hits various buttons in an attempt to shut the noise off, but is unsuccessful. He abruptly gives up and leaves the room.*)

*10. THE RECEPTION ROOM.*

(SUSAN *and* BARBARA *are busy trying to ruck up the carpet behind the barricade. Having completed this, they stand back to survey what they have done.*)

BARBARA: There, it won't hold them for long, but it is something. The gesture of defiance has been made.

(SUSAN *unscrews another leg from one of the stools and hands it to* BARBARA.)

SUSAN: And you take this. If we do get free again and smash these seeing eyes wherever we go, it won't be nearly so easy for them finding us.

BARBARA: Good girl. How do you feel now?

SUSAN: Much better. Much more optimistic.

(*She smiles.*)

BARBARA: We've begun to fight, that's why.

*11. A TUNNEL UNDER THE MOUNTAIN.*

(*The tunnel joins a metal shaft which goes up into the building. There are metal rungs built into the wall of the shaft. It is very dark.* THE DOCTOR *arrives first and waits. Then* IAN *arrives, carrying* TABON *on his back. He dumps* TABON *down on the floor.* TABON *feels around at the base of the shaft.*)

TABON: The switch was somewhere here.

(*He locates the switch and light floods down from the shaft above.*)

I am sorry about the cramps.

IAN: After seven years on your back, what did you expect? Is this it?

TABON: Yes.

THE DOCTOR: We get our breath back and Tabon can tell us what is up there.

IAN: You two stay here if you want to. I'm going up.

(*He puts one foot on a rung and starts to climb, but* THE DOCTOR *grabs his foot and pulls him back.*)

THE DOCTOR: No, Ian. We've got to assume the two girls are still unharmed and plan things as best we can. We won't be much help to them if we're caught again.

IAN:        Alright. What's up there?

TABON:      First, the shaft is at least a hundred feet deep and
            must be climbed every inch of the way. If one of us
            falls...

IAN:        Yes, he's had it. And above the shaft?

TABON:      Is the old atomic magazine. We actually climb into
            it.

            (IAN *and* THE DOCTOR *look worriedly at each
            other*.)

IAN:        The *what* sort of magazine?

TABON:      Atomic. It means...

IAN:        We know what it means. My own people on Earth
            have got that far.

TABON:      There is nothing to fear. When we stopped using
            these devices on Luxor, they were sent here to be
            rendered harmless by my Derivitrons. This was the
            only way it could be done with complete mechanical
            certainty there would be no mistake.

IAN:        And the Derivitrons knew how to do this?

TABON:      I have just said so. There is no danger. They were
            programmed with full knowledge of the devices and
            they made them inactive. Will I go on? You both
            look so uncertain, yet I assure you...

IAN:        Tabon, one moment. If your Derivitrons, with full
            knowledge of the devices, could make them harm-
            less... then presumably, if they were ordered to do
            so, they could make them active again.

TABON:      Yes. If they were ordered to.

IAN: And there'd be enough stuff up there to blow this whole place, this whole mountain, off the face of the planet?

TABON: If they were all rearmed, yes. But you don't know the Derivitron mind, gentlemen. First the order would have to come from a higher being...

THE DOCTOR: The Perfect One ordered it.

TABON: No! This cannot be!

IAN: He told us so, and we believe him.

TABON: But to put himself in such peril is so illogical... No, he would never act this way. I'm sorry. You have been deceived.

IAN: Tabon, listen. The Derivitrons made him because collectively they knew what was going on in your mind... right?

TABON: That is what I believe.

IAN: They need a being superior to themselves to kind of link their thought processes together.

TABON: Not any superior being. Only me, because they were each of them, my creations.

IAN: Okay, with you out of the way... supposing The Perfect One was damaged... he fell over and concussed his electronic brain or something. You weren't there to give him full knowledge and he was no longer able to order them. Could they repair him?

TABON: No.

THE DOCTOR: Then it is true. He has acted logically in the most effective way he could. Tabon, it isn't only that he has ordered these devices rearmed... in some way he has linked his own brainwaves to them, so that if anything damages him...

(TABON *looks at them in horror and buries his face in his hands.*)

IAN: Tabon, it's not hopeless. We know where the device is now. Could you disarm it?

TABON: Don't you see what he has done? He cannot be destroyed!

IAN: But at this end. Up there...

TABON: No. If it is linked to his brain then it is as though it were part of his brain. To interfere with that is to interfere with him.

THE DOCTOR: And will produce the same result?

TABON: Yes. It is my insane dream of being God, carried to its logical end. The existence of everything and everyone here depends wholly and solely on him. He is the necessary centre of life, animate and inanimate, on this planet. We cannot even defy him. My friends, don't you realise this... it is pointless us going any further.

IAN: You mean turn back?

TABON: We have to. We cannot save your women. There can be no final victory for us, because he has only to destroy himself and he destroys us too.

THE DOCTOR: Did you destroy yourself seven years ago when you ran from here? Tabon, you did not. You were a coward. You hid from death in a prolonged artificial sleep. And after the model of whose brain, whose personality, is this creature fashioned? After *yours*, Tabon. After yours. We will go up this shaft, the three of us. And we will rely for our victory on this fact... stake everything on it... That what was impossible for you seven years ago, is impossible for him now.

(*He puts his foot on the bottom rung.*)

I will go first. Then you, Tabon. Then the strong young Ian to support two old men.

(*He climbs further up and* IAN *pushes* TABON *forward to begin the climb.*)

*12. THE RECEPTION ROOM.*

(BARBARA *is busy pulling a long thread out of the side of the carpet.*)

| | |
|---|---|
| BARBARA: | This should be long enough. Now we'll get that ruck out of the carpet and stretch this across instead. |
| SUSAN: | Is it strong? |
| BARBARA: | Strong enough. Where would you say? |
| SUSAN: | That pipe there, near that... what is it, an air-conditioner... to the leg of that thing. |

(*She indicates a small seat, attached to the wall.*)

| | |
|---|---|
| BARBARA: | There's nowhere else really. Let's hope it isn't too far in, so that when they push down the door they don't push our barricade on our trip wire. |
| SUSAN: | Then we stand by the window? |

BARBARA: And let them come for us.

SUSAN: And hope they don't look down.

BARBARA: Which I've not seen one of them do yet.

SUSAN: Then we run for the door.

BARBARA: In fact, our standard plan of campaign. Cause confusion, because they don't seem to expect the unexpected. Do as much damage as we can.

SUSAN: And then a quick getaway.

BARBARA: Only this time they won't find us so easily.

*(She brandishes the stool leg. The two of them fasten the carpet thread to the two agreed objects so that it is taut. SUSAN pings it. She looks at BARBARA and smiles.)*

SUSAN: I wonder what the stronger, more resourceful sex is doing now.

*13. THE ATOMIC MAGAZINE.*

*(THE DOCTOR and TABON hold a trap door up as IAN climbs through. They lower it down again very carefully.)*

IAN: Phew.

TABON: Wait.

*(He moves to the light fixture, unscrews the ball and tips the liquid out. Then he screws the ball back again. He returns to IAN and THE DOCTOR.)*

Now we cannot be seen or heard.

THE DOCTOR:    Would that be the device?

(*He indicates a circular bench on which there are six large silver globes, each about two feet in diameter. Each is capped with a cone-shaped plate and from the pointed ends of each of these come six cables running into a square black box, which completes the circle of implements around the outer edge of the bench. An aerial extends upwards from this black box. There are various dials on the box and also what seems to be a very large thermometer. In this thermometer the level of liquid can be seen to be constantly rising and falling slightly. Towards the top of the thermometer is what is obviously some sort of danger mark.* TABON *examines the box.*)

TABON:    Yes.

IAN:    And they are?

TABON:    Yes.

THE DOCTOR:    And there is nothing you can do?

TABON:    No. You see this?

(*He indicates the level of the liquid in the thermometer.*)

If I interfered with any part, this would rise. Once beyond that point, and quite literally, nothing in this room would even exist a second afterwards.

IAN:    That is him?

TABON:    Yes.

THE DOCTOR:    It looks so harmless.

IAN:    So if we have to handle him, we do so softly. No sudden jolts.

TABON:    You don't injure him or allow him to so damage himself so that he cannot continue as what he is. At least that is how I would have arranged it.

THE DOCTOR:    Sssssh!

> (*They freeze as they hear the sound of a robot approaching.*)


*14. THE RECEPTION ROOM.*

> (*There is a terrific noise as robots outside try to batter down the door of the room.* SUSAN *and* BAR-BARA *are standing at the far end of the room, by the window. The door begins to move, then the barricade gives further and three robots and* A DERIVITRON *enter. They pause uncertainly.* THE DERIVITRON *indicates the girls.*)

DERIVITRON:    Take them.

> (*The robots start to move forward.*)

PERFECT ONE:    Stop!
(*oov*)

> (*He steps forward into the room.*)

I wish to deal with them myself.

> (*He turns towards the two girls.*)

I wish to understand you better. I wish to understand why you senselessly destroy complex equipment and pay no heed to things of importance. As your lives will soon be mine, it is necessary for you to explain these impulses.

SUSAN:    You will have to come and examine us closely, O Perfect One.

(THE PERFECT ONE *moves forward. As he does so,* BARBARA *suddenly realises the danger and screams a warning to him.*)

BARBARA:    No! Go back! Go back!

(*But it is too late.* THE PERFECT ONE *reaches the trip wire and falls forward. He bangs his head on the floor at their feet and lies still. A low crackling sound can be heard coming from him.*)

*15. THE ATOMIC MAGAZINE*

TABON:    Look!

(*The liquid inside the thermometer is slowly but relentlessly rising up the tube towards the danger mark.*)

Next Episode:
**AN INFINITY OF SURPRISES**

# EPISODE FIVE
# AN INFINITY OF SURPRISES

*1. THE ATOMIC MAGAZINE.*

(*The liquid inside the thermometer is slowly but relentlessly rising up the tube towards the danger mark.* THE DOCTOR, IAN *and* TABON *look on, helpless.*)

*2. THE RECEPTION ROOM.*

(*The robots and* THE DERIVITRON *stand motionless.* SUSAN *and* BARBARA *stand with their hands to their mouths.* THE PERFECT ONE *is lying on the floor and there is a faint crackling sound.*)

*3. THE ATOMIC MAGAZINE.*

(*The liquid continues its slow climb towards the*

*danger mark.*)

IAN:      Can't you stop it?

TABON:      Something has happened to him. We can only pray it will straighten itself out.

IAN:      Can it?

TABON:      Possibly. How can I know?

### 4. *The Reception Room.*

(*SUSAN clings to BARBARA in terror. She points to the robots and* THE DERIVITRON.)

SUSAN:      Look at them. They know.

BARBARA:      Surely there's a chance. Why doesn't he move?

SUSAN:      If we pick him up...

BARBARA:      Don't touch him!

### 5. *The Atomic Magazine.*

THE DOCTOR:      We won't know a thing.

IAN:      Oh God! Oh God, make it stop.

(*The rising liquid is almost at the danger mark, but the rate of its rise is slowing and it stops just short. Then it rises a little further, touching the mark, and begins to drop. The three men give a collective sigh of relief.*)

6. *THE RECEPTION ROOM.*

(THE PERFECT ONE *is slowly getting up and the crackling noise has now stopped. He sees the trip wire, grasps it and snaps it in two. He barks an order at* THE DERIVITRON.)

PERFECT ONE: Make the room as it was.

(THE DERIVITRON *and the robots move to obey.* THE PERFECT ONE *stands silently looking at the two girls, who are too shaken to move. The robots put the settee back in position.*)

Now the audio scan.

(*They start to replace the broken globe and* THE PERFECT ONE *finally addresses the girls.*)

Sit down. Barbara... Susan. I sense the strain that possessed you. You did not intend that for me.

BARBARA: For the purely selfish reason we didn't want to blow ourselves to pieces. Don't think we have any regard for you.

PERFECT ONE: Pieces? There would have been no pieces! A vaporised cloud of radioactive dust, but no pieces. Nothing recognisable as Barbara. Nothing recognisable as Susan.

SUSAN: And nothing recognisable as you.

PERFECT ONE: I would have already ceased to be or the explosion would not have happened.

BARBARA: Where are The Doctor and Mr Chesterton?

PERFECT ONE: They have escaped.

BARBARA:    Escaped!

PERFECT ONE:    To the surface of this dead satellite world. They will find no comfort for their hunger or their thirst, and I have made it impossible for them to re-enter this place. Out there they will die... slowly. It is the way they have chosen.

SUSAN:    You mean, you didn't go after them? Try to bring them back?

PERFECT ONE:    They are of no more use to me. The tests carried out on you assure me my long time of waiting is finished. Soon you will be taken to the chairs again and linked to me... then your lives will be mine. I will be a being then as you are now... independent of the power which animates these mechanical creatures. But greater, far greater than flesh and blood, because my body is not made to slow corruption as yours are. I will live forever.

> (SUSAN *giggles nervously, partly due to the knowledge that* THE DOCTOR *and* IAN *have escaped, partly because of the pomposity of* THE PERFECT ONE'*s speech. He looks at her curiously.*)

BARBARA:    Susan?

SUSAN:    I'm sorry. I can't stop it. I can't. It's him living forever, and Ian and Grandfather free, and... and...

BARBARA:    Susan. Susan.

SUSAN:    Barbara, they're free! They're free!

PERFECT ONE:    I do not understand this reaction. Please explain.

SUSAN:    Ian and Grandfather are free!

BARBARA:    You're not much of an improvement on a Derivitron, are you, Perfect One? A machine's a machine, however much it looks like a man. We've got slimy little animals on Earth, they live at the bottom of muddy pools... there is more humanity in one of them...

PERFECT ONE:    I select the word 'animals'. It has no meaning for me.

BARBARA:    Life has no meaning for you. Oh God, in a tragic way it is funny. I almost hope you do succeed... that you get this enduring life and live forever. Only I want to be there. In however many generations it takes to do it. I want to be there when the novelty wears off and you're bored to death with thinking how wonderful you are.

SUSAN:    Will you make more Perfect Ones? A lot of little Perfect Ones slithering out of their test tubes?

BARBARA:    He won't need to, Susan. He won't get lonely. He can talk to his old Derivitrons.

(*She bows mockingly at* THE PERFECT ONE.)

You have made us well, O Perfect One, and we serve you.

(THE PERFECT ONE *is clearly unsettled by this mockery.*)

PERFECT ONE:    This talk has no meaning for me.

BARBARA:    We're going too fast for you?

PERFECT ONE:    Stop. I order you to stop.

SUSAN:    Order us? Do you think we're Derivitrons?

BARBARA:       Do you think we stop because an electronic puppet tells us to?

SUSAN:         Can't your poor little clockwork brain keep up with us?

PERFECT ONE:   It has no meaning.

BARBARA:       It has meaning enough for us. What do you want us to talk about? All the wonderful surprises you've got in store for us?

SUSAN:         Peter Piper picked a peck of pickled pepper.

BARBARA:       Mary, Mary, quite contrary, how does your garden grow? Tell us, O Perfect One, how does your garden grow?

SUSAN:         Have you got silver bells and cockle shells?

BARBARA:       And two pretty maids in your electric chairs?

               (THE PERFECT ONE *puts his hands over his ears and screams at the robots.*)

PERFECT ONE:   Stop them! Stop them!

               (SUSAN *points at him and laughs.*)

SUSAN:         He's going to live forever!

BARBARA:       Praise be to thee, O Perfect One.

               (SUSAN *and* BARBARA *both laugh until the advancing robots are almost on them, then they both stop. The robots pause. There is a moment of silence as each side waits. The silence is interrupted by* THE PERFECT ONE. *At first his voice is puzzled, struggling to come to terms with a new experience and a new concept.*)

PERFECT ONE: This reaction disturbs me. Words that have no meaning. Ian and The Doctor have escaped to their death and you are glad. I am The Perfect One, conceived in the brain of Tabon, the greatest of all the scientific Masters of Luxor... and this moves you to laughter?

(*He turns to* THE DERIVITRON.)

It is possible their lives are not in harmony with all the scientific principles we have examined in flesh and blood creatures. They must be subjected to more tests before I will undergo the great experiment with them. Take them to the chairs. I will plan the tests now.

(*He exits the room.* THE DERIVITRON *motions to the robots and they lead the two girls from the room.*)

7. *THE ATOMIC MAGAZINE.*

(*The liquid has now dropped considerably and is well away from the danger mark.* THE DOCTOR *addresses* TABON.)

THE DOCTOR: What do you make of it?

TABON: I would say he has suffered a severe shock, possibly brought on by a physical blow of some kind.

IAN: The first one, when it almost went over the top?

TABON: Yes. It cleared itself and returned to normal.

THE DOCTOR: Then began to jump all over the place?

| | |
|---|---|
| TABON: | A period of grave disturbance within the mechanism of the brain, as though new tensions had been set up to which he had to adjust himself. |
| THE DOCTOR: | And this shouldn't happen in the normal life of the creature? |
| TABON: | Not as suddenly as there are recorded here, no. |
| IAN: | Tabon, are we safe now? Can we forget about that thing and do what we came for? |
| TABON: | If we are to do anything of what we came for, we must forget about this. But I don't know when it all might suddenly end... and that's the truth Mr Chesterton. |
| IAN: | How do we find out where Barbara and Susan are? |
| TABON: | In what was once my study, there was a bank of screens. We called it the Audio and Visual Locator Mechanism. |
| IAN: | Closed circuit television. |
| TABON: | It operates through those bulbs. Since I removed the fluid from that one it is inactive. |
| IAN: | And from there I could see anywhere in t his building? |
| TABON: | On a selector console, yes. |
| IAN: | How do I get there? |
| THE DOCTOR: | How *you* get there? |
| IAN: | We've got to split up. You and Tabon stick together while I see what I can find out alone. We can't put all our eggs in one basket. |

THE DOCTOR: Good thinking, my boy. I agree.

IAN: So I've got to know two things. How do I find your old study... and what's the most effective thing you two can be doing, and where?

TABON: Have you something I can use to draw a plan?

(THE DOCTOR *produces a piece of paper and a pen.*)

THE DOCTOR: Here.

(TABON *proceeds to draw a rough map.*)

IAN: What do you think?

THE DOCTOR: Amongst my favourite twentieth century readings were the memoirs of Generals. Diversionary tactics... that's what they taught me. Tabon and I will give them something to think about and take the pressure off you.

IAN: What?

THE DOCTOR: I don't know what. You worry about your side of it.

(TABON *gives the map to* IAN.)

TABON: Here. There's no time for a detailed plan. This is the eighteenth level. The building is circular with a hole through its centre. The two exterior lift shafts are at either end of the diameter...

IAN: Leaving two semi-circles.

TABON: On the eighteenth level one of them has blue flooring and the other yellow. You want the blue. The entry door to my suite of rooms and study was exactly half-way along the blue corridor.

IAN:            I'll find it. The eighteenth level. Where are we now?

TABON:          What would be minus ten. So you have to climb through twenty-eight levels. Don't take either of the lifts, because in there you can be trapped. Take the stairs. Neither robots nor Derivitrons can handle themselves happily on stairs. Out of that door, turn right. The staircase is behind the barred door.

IAN:            Any idea what you might do?

                (*As* IAN *moves towards the door,* THE DOCTOR *looks questioningly at* TABON.)

TABON:          I think power. The Derivitrons have obviously modified the generators to take all the power from the supply ships. If I can get some of it flooding back into your TARDIS, I might put some of them out of action and give you the means of escape.

IAN:            Then we all head for the TARDIS when we've done what we can. Good luck.

                (*He leaves the room.*)

THE DOCTOR:     If it is not already too late...

                (TABON *puts his hand on* THE DOCTOR's *shoulder and tries to comfort him.*)

TABON:          You gave me hope, friend...

THE DOCTOR:     These new tensions you spoke of... in The Perfect One?

TABON:          Your women? No.

THE DOCTOR:     You can't be sure, Tabon. You can't be sure.

TABON:          Do you only have courage for the sake of the young man?

THE DOCTOR: My Granddaughter is all I have.

TABON: Then we must tear down this place to save her.

THE DOCTOR: Yes. Ian should be clear now. Lead the way.

(TABON *leaves the room, with* THE DOCTOR *following him.*)

*8. THE PERFECT ONE'S STUDY.*

(A DERIVITRON *is testing the bank of screens as* THE PERFECT ONE *enters. All of the screens are now working except one.* THE DERIVITRON *is turning this one on and off, trying to make it work.* THE PERFECT ONE *enters the room, pushes* THE DERIVITRON *out of the way, and tries the switch himself. He reads the location marked beneath the screen.*)

PERFECT ONE: This is the atomic magazine.

DERIVITRON: Yes, Perfect One.

PERFECT ONE: Replace the vision eye, at once.

DERIVITRON: Yes, Perfect One.

(THE PERFECT ONE *continues to look at the blank screen for a moment, then he leaves it and goes over to his desk. As he does so the image of* IAN *passes across one of the working screens.* THE PERFECT ONE *sits at his desk. He is examining a piece of paper on which a graph shows the results of* SUSAN *and* BARBARA's *reactions to the previous test. On another piece of paper he begins to write down symbols which indicate the new tests he is preparing.*)

9. *THE LABORATORY.*

(SUSAN *and* BARBARA *are once again laying on the trolleys, but this time they are strapped down.* THE DERIVITRON *and two robots are busily preparing the chairs.*)

SUSAN:      They'll find a way back in. They must find a way back in...

BARBARA:    I know what they've gone after. The signal, Susan. The signal that brought us here. It would have to be something that would make them leave... otherwise it would be suicide.

SUSAN:      Then we've got to survive whatever new tests he works out for us... we've got to.

BARBARA:    Yes. Let's be thankful it's more tests and not the big blast off.

SUSAN:      He seemed to go to pieces as soon as we began talking nonsense.

BARBARA:    But that's it. In his world everything is scientific, cause and effect... even ordinary conversation. And deadly dull into the bargain. When you began to laugh it opened up a whole new range of weapons against The Perfect One.

SUSAN:      I couldn't help it. Barbara, how can we use it now?

BARBARA:    Would it work on the Derivitron and the robots?

SUSAN:      Yes. We've got to delay them.

BARBARA:    It's more than just laughing. They must be geared to
            the expected reactions of the Luxorites.

SUSAN:      Lordly disdain, and at the last moment, holy terror.

BARBARA:    It's confusion. We've got to do something they can't
            possibly expect us to do.

SUSAN:      Something altogether new.

BARBARA:    Think Susan, think.

            (*The robots and* THE DERIVITRON *complete the
            preparation of the chairs. Then, as* THE DERIVIT-
            RON *indicates to the robots that they should bring
            the girls to the chairs,* BARBARA *begins to sing.*
            SUSAN *quickly joins in.*)

            Land of hope and glory...

            (*The robots approach the girls. They move to hold
            them, but then pause uncertainly.*)

BARBARA AND  ... How can we extol thee, who are born of thee...
SUSAN:

            (*The robots back away.*)

            Wider still and wider, shall thy bounds be set...

THE DERIVITRON: This Derivitron does not understand the meaning of
            these words.

BARBARA AND  God who made thee mighty, make thee mightier
SUSAN:       yet... God who made thee mighty...

            *10. THE PERFECT ONE'S STUDY.*

(THE PERFECT ONE *stands before the bank of screens and watches in amazement as the girls continue to sing. The sound echoes around the room.*)

BARBARA AND
SUSAN
(*on screen*):
Make thee mightier yet.

(*There is a brief pause and then they start up again*)

Onward Christian soldiers, marching as to war...

(THE PERFECT ONE *hurriedly leaves his study.*)

*11. A CORRIDOR OUTSIDE THE PERFECT ONE'S STUDY.*

(THE PERFECT ONE *comes out, shuts the door and strides off out of view. A robot remains on guard outside. Further along the corridor,* IAN'*s head appears around a corner from a staircase and looks towards the robot. He steps into full view.*)

IAN:
Hey Buster! Come and get me!

(*The robot turns towards* IAN *and trundles menacingly towards him with its arms outstretched. When it is almost on him,* IAN *throws himself to one side and down, then he heaves himself up, shouldering the robot towards the staircase. The robot crashes down the stairs, arms flailing.* IAN *runs down the corridor to the door of the study and cautiously opens the door.*)

*12. THE PERFECT ONE'S STUDY.*

(IAN *enters. He hears the sound of* BARBARA *and* SUSAN *singing and moves over to the view screens. His face lights up as he sees that they are alive and unharmed.*)

IAN: Thank God for that! You little beauties, you little beauties!

(*His joy is short-lived, however, and suddenly he stiffens in alarm, as* THE PERFECT ONE *comes into view on the screen.*)

*13. THE LABORATORY.*

(THE PERFECT ONE *strides across to* BARBARA *and* SUSAN. *He has in his hand a small spray can. He points it at their faces and as a fine mist envelopes them, they stop singing.*)

PERFECT ONE: You can hear me now... yes, you can hear me, but you cannot speak.

(*He turns to* THE DERIVITRON.)

See the fear in their eyes... see it. I have witless machines to serve me. Senseless automatons. When life is mine and all the powers of Tabon who made me, I will build better things than you. Not dull circuits that cannot think more than they are programmed to think.

(*He turns back to* BARBARA *and* SUSAN.)

The drug paralyses your muscles, but you can hear. You can confuse these stunted creatures with your deliberate disorder... but I am The Perfect One. Had you forgotten that? I adjust to your thoughts quicker than you expected.

(*He turns and almost screams at* THE DERIVITRON *and the robots.*)

The meaning of their words is that they have no meaning. There will be no further tests.

DERIVITRON: This Derivitron understands and obeys.

PERFECT ONE: I will take their lives now. Get them in the chairs.

(*The robots advance once more on the girls.*)

*14. THE CORRIDOR OUTSIDE THE PERFECT ONE'S STUDY.*

(*Two robots look down the stairs. They turn and hurry towards the study door.* IAN *opens the door and they lunge towards him, but he slams it shut.*)

*15. THE PERFECT ONE'S STUDY.*

(IAN *pulls a lever beside the door, which apparently locks it.*)

IAN: What do I do? What do I do?

(*He goes over to the view screens and examines the various controls. He notices a microphone with a switch beneath it.*)

*16. THE LABORATORY.*

(SUSAN *is being lifted from the trolley she is on to one of the chairs. Suddenly* IAN'*s voice booms out into the room.*)

IAN (*oov*):      Hold it, Perfect One.

PERFECT ONE:      Ian!

IAN:      The name is Chesterton to you... Mr Chesterton. Unless you're one of my friends, then it's Ian. But you're not my friend. You're not anybody's friend. You haven't got a friend in the world.

PERFECT ONE:      He is in my quarters. Leave these. Get him.

(*The robots move to obey.*)

*17. THE PERFECT ONE'S STUDY.*

(*As* IAN *speaks there is a crashing sound outside the door.*)

IAN:      Just a pack of mouldy old iron men. But I could be your friend if you'd let me. I could give you what those women can't give you... I could give you a man's life, Perfect One. A man's life.

*18. THE LABORATORY.*

(*As the robots are about to leave the room,* THE PERFECT ONE *barks a new order.*)

PERFECT ONE:      Stay!

IAN (*oov*):      You don't know about women, do you? These are

Earth women. They are inferior creatures. You take life from them and you will be as weak as they are. You don't believe me? Ask Tabon how you can live the life of flesh and blood creatures. He knows more about you then you do yourself.

PERFECT ONE: Tabon!

IAN (*oov*): Tabon, Scientific Master of the Masters of Luxor. Exalted Lord of Urdanna. Warden of the High District. He's the one isn't he? The big brain who dreamed you up out of bits of wire and transistors.

PERFECT ONE: Tabon is dead. He escaped to death on the dead planet.

IAN (*oov*): He is alive. The Doctor and I, we've spoken to him. He told us about the one hidden fault in your construction... something you don't even know yourself is there.

PERFECT ONE: False! False! Unacceptable! False! It is seven years. Tabon could not live that long.

### 19. *THE PERFECT ONE'S STUDY.*

IAN: That's the life of a man for you... enduring life. And the life of Earth men is ten times stronger than that of Luxorites. You were made to the model of a man, Perfect One... that's where Tabon says you're making your big mistake now. If you don't believe me... link yourself to those inferior creatures and find out.

(*The door bursts open and the robots come at him. He tries to throw one off balance, but the other manages to grab him and holds him in a bear hug.*)

PERFECT ONE
(*oov*):

Chesterton! Chesterton! Tabon is dead. False Chesterton. False, the one who made me is...

(THE PERFECT ONE'*s voice is cut off as one of the robots goes to the console and cuts off the speaker.*)

*20. THE LABORATORY.*

(THE PERFECT ONE *stands at the door as* THE DERIV-ITRON *and the robots leave.*)

PERFECT ONE: Get him and bring him here. Get him.

(*He moves over to* BARBARA *and* SUSAN.)

Even in that moment I came into being I knew the mind of Tabon of Luxor. He was the one I would not have destroyed. See how different I am made from these machines... he made them too, yet they did not know his mind... he gave them their stunted lives and they felt nothing for him. I searched for him... the perfect creature of science searched for the perfect man of science... Yes, I am weak, you women of Earth. I long for my home as other true living creatures do, but my home is not here... not on Luxor. My home is in the brain of Tabon. Chesterton lies. Tabon is dead. Killed by the other Masters because I was conceived to replace them all. Only I was his equal. He was more than flesh and blood... he was God. Do you think if he had lived these seven years he would have hidden himself from me?

(*The effects of the drug spray are starting to wear*

*off and* BARBARA *struggles to mumble something.*)

BARBARA: The Derivitrons made you.

(THE PERFECT ONE *grabs her arm and stares close-ly at her.*)

You told us the Derivitrons made you.

(*He releases her.*)

PERFECT ONE: They did what they knew they must do.

(*The robots and* THE DERIVITRON *enter with* IAN. *His arms are bound to his side.*)

IAN: Let the women go, Perfect One. You're made as a man... experiment on me.

BARBARA: No, Ian!

(*She turns to* THE PERFECT ONE.)

He's doing this to save us.

PERFECT ONE: I decide what is done here. Strap him in the chair.

(*The robots do as instructed.*)

You force me to new experiences, Mr Chesterton... to use the chairs in a way I have never used them before. As Barbara and Susan will tell you, the level of power I use for experiments immediately robs a person of consciousness... and so of pain.

IAN: Let's have it without the talk, buster.

PERFECT ONE: But we must have talk. We must have knowledge and truth. Where did you learn of Tabon? How did you get back in here from the surface of the planet? Will you tell me these things of your own accord?

IAN: The truth won't be acceptable, therefore you won't believe it.

PERFECT ONE: A degree of power that will keep you conscious...

IAN: The word is torture. You should get a kick out of it. It's a weapon used by the lower forms of life when they get big ideas about themselves.

PERFECT ONE: Tabon is dead! There is no imperfection in me. Your words are false!

IAN: Tabon is alive. It was his signal that brought us here, the signal you couldn't trace.

PERFECT ONE: There was no signal!

IAN: It wasn't operating while this place has power to pick it up. He had it fixed to stop the ships coming in from Luxor, but it didn't work with them. It only worked with us.

PERFECT ONE: None of it is acceptable. Tabon is dead!

IAN: Why has he got to be dead?

PERFECT ONE: Because I am the son of his brain. He would love me as a father loves his most perfect child.

IAN: He hates you, Perfect One. You're the most shameful creation a man of science has ever made.

PERFECT ONE: No!

IAN: Yes. He didn't make you himself because you had become the image of everything he detested in his science.

PERFECT ONE: No!

(*He leaps at the console, where* THE DERIVITRON *is*

*operating the controls and pushes it roughly aside. He twists the power dial up to maximum.)*

BARBARA: Don't do it!

*(IAN's helmet begins to glow. He lets out a gasp, then clenches his fists and his teeth.)*

### 21. THE POWER CONTROL ROOM.

*(A large panel covered with switches, dials and wildly flickering needles fills one wall of the room. A loud hum pervades the air. A DERIVITRON studies the various instruments, then leaves the room.)*

### 22. A CORRIDOR OUTSIDE THE POWER CONTROL ROOM.

*(THE DERIVITRON moves off down the corridor. He does not notice THE DOCTOR and TABON crouching down at the top of a staircase. They wait there until he turns a corner.)*

THE DOCTOR: He didn't see us.

TABON: They have not been put on alert.

THE DOCTOR: That's the power room he came out of?

TABON: Yes. He'll come back. If he's still programmed to the same checking routine, we have about twenty minutes.

THE DOCTOR: Come on.

*(They both go towards the door.)*


23. *The Laboratory.*

*(IAN's tortured face is bathed in sweat, as the helmet glows brightly.)*

PERFECT ONE:     Enough.

*(THE DERIVITRON at the console turns off the power. IAN slumps forward. THE PERFECT ONE goes over to him and pushes back his head.)*

How did you find your way back in here? Where is The Doctor?

IAN:     What do you want me to say? I'll say it.

PERFECT ONE:     The truth.

IAN:     Go and find the old cemetery where we found Tabon... That's where they both are.

SUSAN:     Leave him alone and go and look for them.

BARBARA:     You will kill him this way!

PERFECT ONE:     You and The Doctor found the dead body of Tabon!

IAN:     You want me to say that?

PERFECT ONE:     It's the truth.

IAN:     And if I say it... what happens then?

PERFECT ONE:     You are freed from pain and I take life from these women as I planned.

IAN:     He was in a tomb... he'd been asleep for seven years. He hates you, Perfect One. He wants to destroy you.

(THE PERFECT ONE *slaps* IAN's *face*.)

PERFECT ONE:    False, Chesterton. Lies!

IAN:    Like it or not, you're going to have to accept it. They're fixing the signal now to contact the ships of Luxor. Your rule here is nearly over.

(THE PERFECT ONE *moves back to the console and turns up the power again.* IAN's *helmet starts to glow*.)

24. *THE POWER CONTROL ROOM*.

(TABON *pulls down a panel on the control console. He stops when he sees one of the needles start to flicker*.)

TABON:    That is power to the central laboratory.

(THE DOCTOR *and* TABON *look at each other and suddenly* THE DOCTOR *looks up at the globe above them. He quickly stretches up and is about to unscrew it*.)

25. *THE PERFECT ONE'S STUDY*.

(A DERIVITRON *watches in alarm as he sees* TABON *and* THE DOCTOR *in the power control room. He operates a switch and immediately an alarm siren sounds*.)

26. *A CORRIDOR*.

DERIVITRON    Emergency alert. Emergency alert. Section, Power

| | |
|---|---|
| (*oov*): | Transformer Unit. This Derivitron registers the pres ence of Tabon. The presence of Tabon... |

(A DERIVITRON *in the corridor turns and moves away*)

27. *THE LABORATORY.*

(THE PERFECT ONE *stands with his hand on the power switch. He looks up as the voice continues.*)

| | |
|---|---|
| DERIVITRON (*oov*): | ... and stranger, name programmed, The Doctor. Emergency alert. Emergency alert. Section, Power Transformer Unit. This Derivitron registers the presence of Tabon. The presence of Tabon, and stranger, name programmed, The Doctor. |

(THE PERFECT ONE *is stunned. He turns off the power.*)

| | |
|---|---|
| PERFECT ONE: | Tabon is alive! |

28. *THE POWER CONTROL ROOM.*

(TABON *is working furiously, turning sections of wire back to front behind one of the panels. The sirens can be heard.*)

| | |
|---|---|
| THE DOCTOR: | Move, Tabon, move or your machines will be on us. |
| TABON: | I've got to order it so they won't know straight away what I've done. |
| THE DOCTOR: | We should have fixed that bulb as soon as we came in. |
| TABON: | It would not have altered anything. We were fortu- |

nate we were not seen earlier.

THE DOCTOR: What will this do?

TABON: Run a slow feedback of power into your TARDIS.

(*He closes up the panel.*)

I can't do anything else from here. We can't hide any longer... they'll come in here and take us. Doctor, help me. They'll take us before him and I can't face him... I can't.

THE DOCTOR: What can I do to stop it?

(TABON *reaches inside the pouch at his waist and produces an ornamental knife.*)

TABON: Kill me now. I have helped you. Don't you see it... my creature cannot be destroyed.

(THE DOCTOR *knocks the knife out of* TABON'*s hand and it clatters to the floor.*)

THE DOCTOR: Who are we to say what can't be done? Listen to me, Tabon. I have visited more worlds and lived amongst stranger people than you have ever dreamed of... the man who says "This will be" or "That cannot possibly be", he has never looked at life since he was born.

TABON: This is not life... it is a machine!

THE DOCTOR: We are alive. We are beings programmed to an infinity of surprises.

(*They hear the sound of robots approaching from outside.*)

29. *The Laboratory.*

(THE PERFECT ONE *is being strapped into his chair by* THE DERIVITRON. *Then the helmet is placed over his head.*)

PERFECT ONE: Do it faster. I do not need the straps.

BARBARA: You can never do it this way, Perfect One. Look at him, you've nearly killed him already.

SUSAN: Everything he told you was to win time for us and the others.

PERFECT ONE: I will face my masters as a whole living man. The helmet. The helmet!

(IAN, *who is barely conscious, mumbles to himself.*)

IAN: What's he gonna do? What's he gonna do?

BARBARA: Ian, Ian... he's going to take your life for nothing. We can't help you.

(*She screams out.*)

Help! Help!

SUSAN: Let us up from here. Don't, Perfect One. Don't!

(*As she is begging for* IAN's *life,* SUSAN *is desperately struggling to free her arms from the trolley straps. One of the straps is slightly looser than the others.*)

PERFECT ONE: Full power! Full power through him to me. I will face my master with life in me... Enduring life!

(SUSAN *manages to free one arm.*)

DERIVITRON:     I obey.

> (*He turns the switch to maximum. The power noise once again builds up and the helmets on* IAN*'s and* THE PERFECT ONE*'s heads begin to glow.* IAN*'s mouth opens in a silent scream.*)

Next Episode:
### THE FLOWER BLOOMS

# EPISODE SIX

# THE FLOWER BLOOMS

*1. THE LABORATORY.*

(IAN *is strapped to the chair, the helmet on his head glowing brightly.* THE PERFECT ONE *is similarly seated but, unlike* IAN, *has a rapt, expectant expression on his face. On the other side of the laboratory,* SUSAN *struggles free of her bonds and, jumping down from the trolley, rushes at* THE DERIVITRON *that is standing by the console. She hurtles into him and, catching him off-guard, manages to push him aside for long enough to turn the power control back to off.*)

PERFECT ONE:    Get her!

(THE DERIVITRON *quickly recovers, but as he rushes at her, she goes down on her hands and knees and trips him up. He crashes to the ground.* SUSAN *runs over to* IAN *and unclips the bands which hold him to the chair.* IAN *slumps forward.*)

SUSAN: Ian, Ian!

BARBARA: Ian, come out of it. Susan, slap his face.

(*As* THE PERFECT ONE *struggles free of his chair and helmet,* SUSAN *slaps* IAN's *face. Then* THE PERFECT ONE *grabs her and holds her back as she struggles. In doing so she forces him back away from* IAN, *who is gradually regaining consciousness.* IAN *recovers enough to see that* THE PERFECT ONE *has* SUSAN *in his grasp.*)

PERFECT ONE: Stay there, Mr Chesterton. You know what will happen if you attack me.

IAN: I know what will happen if I don't. We've got nothing to lose now.

(*As* IAN *is talking, the robots move behind him.*)

SUSAN: Ian, behind you!

IAN: Hold it! There's nothing a man won't do when he's desperate, Perfect One. Order these T-models back or so help me I'll come at you. I can move faster than they can... or you.

PERFECT ONE: Back. Leave Chesterton alone.

(*He releases* SUSAN.)

I can be patient. In the end, none of you can defeat me.

(SUSAN *goes over to* BARBARA *and releases her.* IAN *moves beside them both.* BARBARA *hugs him.*)

BARBARA:       Ian. Thank God you're alive.

IAN:           And Susan.

               (THE PERFECT ONE *has begun edging towards the
               robots and* THE DERIVITRON *near the door.* IAN
               *sees what he is doing.*)

               Don't try it. On Earth we have a thing called a rugby
               tackle. I could bring you down before you reached
               the door.

PERFECT ONE:   Of course.

IAN:           You've saddled yourself with a two-edged weapon.

PERFECT ONE:   It will pass. Now you are reckless, Chesterton, and
               even their lives mean nothing. Soon I shall walk
               from here and you will not harm me. You are flesh
               and blood and therefore you are not constant.

IAN:           Don't bank on it.

PERFECT ONE:   Look at your women. They are your weakness.

IAN:           And Tabon is yours. Before, it didn't matter to you if
               you blew this whole place to smithereens. It matters
               now.

BARBARA:       Your home is in the brain of Tabon and he lives.

IAN:           So who's bluffing who, Perfect One? Who's bluffing
               who?

               *2. A CORRIDOR.*

               (A DERIVITRON *and two robots escort* THE DOCTOR
               *and* TABON *down the corridor.*)

### 3. THE LABORATORY.

(THE DERIVITRON *and the robots are still standing by the door, with* THE PERFECT ONE *nearby.* IAN, SUSAN *and* BARBARA *are standing by the trolleys.*)

BARBARA: Look at him. Should we feel sorry for him?

IAN: Not unless you've been dehumanised as he has.

SUSAN: Grandfather called him "the mockery of a man".

BARBARA: Does Tabon really hate him?

(IAN *nods.*)

IAN: He experimented on his own people... killed hundreds of them to make that, then he began to see he was developing the kind of creature he had become himself. The Perfect One was complete, living in his mind, when he fled from the very idea of him.

SUSAN: But if he hadn't killed all those people in his experiments... would it still have been wrong to have made The Perfect One... a real person?

IAN: Can you answer that?

(*He looks at* BARBARA.)

SUSAN: If he'd done it by lawful means?

BARBARA: I can only feel the answer. And maybe it's only for me. Deep inside us we battle with ourselves... there is a perfection from which we come and all our lives, we... we strive to re-create it... as though it was a plan written into our bones. Does it sound too simple to say happiness is when we succeed, misery and despair when we fail?

SUSAN:           Why are you Earth people afraid of the word 'God'?

IAN:             Perhaps because he is no longer scientific.

BARBARA:         He waits for his God, and his God is only a man.

                 (*She turns to* IAN *and he holds her.*)

                 I can't bear to watch it.

                 (IAN *looks at* SUSAN *over* BARBARA'*s shoulder.*)

IAN:             Does that answer your question?

                 *4. OUTSIDE THE LABORATORY.*

                 (THE DOCTOR *and* TABON, *escorted by* THE DERIVIT-
                 RON *and the two robots, approach the door. The
                 door opens and they enter.*)

                 *5. THE LABORATORY.*

                 (*For a moment the two groups stand looking at
                 each other.*)

PERFECT ONE:     Free them.

DERIVITRON:      This Derivitron does not understand.

PERFECT ONE:     Free them!

                 (*As they are freed,* SUSAN *runs to* THE DOCTOR.)

SUSAN:           Grandfather! Grandfather!

THE DOCTOR:      Susan, you're safe. Thank God you're safe.

(THE PERFECT ONE *glares at* THE DOCTOR.)

PERFECT ONE: Get with the other Earth people.

TABON: No friend, don't leave me. Please don't leave me. I can't face him. Look at me, I've no courage for myself. I can't face him.

THE DOCTOR: Susan, go back to the others. Quickly.

(SUSAN *returns to* IAN *and* BARBARA)

PERFECT ONE: I gave an order, Doctor... it is to be obeyed.

(THE DOCTOR *turns to* TABON.)

THE DOCTOR: I won't leave you.

PERFECT ONE: Doctor, I must be obeyed!

THE DOCTOR: Not by me. I'm not one of your senseless machines.

PERFECT ONE: In this place I hold the power of life and death over machines and men alike.

THE DOCTOR: Wrong. Only the power of death. You cannot give life to flesh and blood creatures.

PERFECT ONE: Your words have no meaning.

THE DOCTOR: I'll tell you what they mean. The one who gives life holds the power of life. And this is the man who gave life to you, Perfect One. Tabon of Luxor. This is the time of your obedience.

(TABON *meanwhile gathers enough courage to move towards* THE PERFECT ONE. *Then he kneels before him.*)

TABON: Let these people go. I beg you, put power back in their ship and let them go.

(THE PERFECT ONE *backs away in horror before him.*)

I will stay here. You can do anything you like with me. Experiment on me. Take my life. Only let them go free.

PERFECT ONE:    Don't kneel before me.

TABON:    I have cost too many good lives already. Let them go to their own world.

PERFECT ONE:    Don't kneel. Don't kneel. We are equals, master... you and I, we are equals.

TABON:    Let them go.

PERFECT ONE:    Their lives are worthless. We will use them all to make others.

TABON:    No. No.

PERFECT ONE:    You and I together. We can study the women.

TABON:    No.

PERFECT ONE:    You did not go away because you hate me. You needed time to think. To make new plans.

TABON:    No.

PERFECT ONE:    It isn't true what the Earthman says... that you hate me... that I am your shame.

TABON:    Set them free.

(THE PERFECT ONE *grabs* TABON.)

PERFECT ONE:    Say it isn't true! Say it isn't true!

TABON:    If I could I would destroy you.

PERFECT ONE:    No... No!

(*He pushes* TABON *away in horror.*)

BARBARA: If I could make you like us... I would. I don't hate you.

PERFECT ONE: You say that?

BARBARA: I don't hate you.

PERFECT ONE: The ships from Luxor don't come any more... and when the power we have stored from you is gone, these ones and I... we will stand... we will stand. That is how he made us. These ones don't know... but I know.

THE DOCTOR: They made you... not Tabon.

PERFECT ONE: I will see nothing... hear nothing... feel nothing.

THE DOCTOR: The more he thought about you, the more he knew just that.

PERFECT ONE: Was I made to be a statue?

TABON: I didn't make you.

PERFECT ONE: You made these.

(*He indicates the robots.*)

Did you expect them to see me as clearly as you did? These poor machines wanted to serve one of their own kind. They made me because they loved me. I am The Perfect One. I am their absolute master. If they feel any pride it is all in me, and you say they have condemned me?

TABON: I condemned you. When I first dreamed of making a man, I condemned you then.

PERFECT ONE: I am a machine, the same as these, I can never be more?

TABON: No. I can't give you more. I could only create in you what I had created in myself.

(THE PERFECT ONE *grabs* TABON'*s hands.*)

PERFECT ONE: Then your hands must destroy me.

(TABON *struggles to get free.*)

TABON: If I harm you I destroy us all.

PERFECT ONE: Destroy me.

(THE DOCTOR *and* IAN *join in the struggle, trying to pull them apart.*)

TABON: You know I can't do it.

PERFECT ONE: I lied. I am not linked to any device. I said it for my own protection.

IAN: We've seen it in the atomic magazine.

(THE PERFECT ONe *breaks free and turns to* THE DERIVITRONS *and robots.*)

PERFECT ONE: Destroy me! This is the last command I give you. Destroy The Perfect One.

(THE DERIVITRONS *and the robots move uncertainly towards* THE PERFECT ONE.)

TABON: Get back. Get back. You listened to my orders once. Get back!

(THE DOCTOR *and* IAN *join* TABON *who is standing between the robots and* THE PERFECT ONE.)

PERFECT ONE: They serve me now.

(THE DOCTOR *tries to reason with* THE DERIVITRONS)

THE DOCTOR: You'll blow yourselves to pieces, and all of us.

PERFECT ONE: You are ordered to destroy this worthless machine.

(TABON *suddenly seems to come alive again and, summoning all his old authority, addresses* THE DERIVITRONS.)

TABON: I am Tabon, master of the Masters of Luxor. You will obey me.

(*The line of robots stop in front of* TABON *and all speak in unison.*)

DERIVITRONS: This Derivitron does not understand the command.

(IAN *looks at* THE PERFECT ONE.)

IAN: They don't obey you. What do you do now?

THE DOCTOR: Be grateful you are what you are. You have been raised above the level of nothing at all.

(THE PERFECT ONE *stands in anguish, moaning, his hands pressed to his head.*)

PERFECT ONE: I can't think. I can't think.

DERIVITRONS: This Derivitron does not understand the command.

(*After beginning this chant in unison, the synchronisation gradually breaks up until between them all that can be heard is a jumble of noise.* THE PERFECT ONE'*s voice rises above the din.*)

PERFECT ONE: Stop them. I order them to stop.

(THE DOCTOR *whispers to* SUSAN *and* BARBARA.)

| | |
|---|---|
| THE DOCTOR: | Don't stop to ask questions. Get out of here. Get down to the courtyard. We've got power flowing back into the TARDIS. Hurry. |
| SUSAN: | What about you and Ian and Tabon? |
| THE DOCTOR: | We will come. Go now! |

(*The two girls obey and hurry out of the door.* THE DERIVITRONS *continue to chant and* THE PERFECT ONE *continues to hold his head and moan.* THE DOCTOR *turns his attention to* IAN.)

| | |
|---|---|
| | We've got power flowing back into the TARDIS. |
| IAN: | You can't have! |
| THE DOCTOR: | Tabon reversed some of the flow in the power control room. |

(*He turns to* TABON.)

| | |
|---|---|
| | Is that what's causing this? |
| TABON: | It is not the main factor. I don't think they were ever reprogrammed not to accept a command from me. That, and for the first time they have been ordered to destroy themselves. |
| IAN: | Too much for them. What about him? |
| TABON: | I don't know. |
| THE DOCTOR: | If he ceases to be what he is, while the power is flowing, he sets off the explosion. Is this it? |
| IAN: | He calls himself a machine. He didn't talk like that when we met him. |
| TABON: | Yes, it could be. It could be. |

IAN:        How much power does the TARDIS need to get going?

THE DOCTOR:        Not much. If we can get within the influence of a sun, we can recharge completely there.

IAN:        Then what the hell are we waiting here for?

> (THE PERFECT ONE *is still ranting on, his voice getting louder and louder, as he addresses no one in particular.*)

PERFECT ONE:        Masters of Luxor... I have killed you all! All of you dead... killed by your own machines. Tabon is back. Tabon who made me is coming. I do not serve. Ah! Ah! Aaaaargh! I do not serve. The Perfect One does not serve!

> (THE DOCTOR *and* IAN *try to drag* TABON *away from this spectacle, but* TABON *refuses and stands there, his eyes fixed on* THE PERFECT ONE.)

THE DOCTOR:        Tabon, there's nothing you can do for him.

> (*He looks at* IAN.)

We can't leave him.

TABON:        I condemned him to this. It was me. I condemned him.

IAN:        Remember what we saw in the atomic magazine room. This whole place is going up!

TABON:        You shouldn't have brought me back. You should have left me sleeping.

IAN:        For God's sake! We didn't have a chance then... we've got one now.

TABON:        Leave me here. Save yourselves.

              (*Without warning,* IAN *hits* TABON *on the jaw, who falls to the ground, unconscious.*)

IAN:          Sorry! Help me get him up.

              (*As* THE DOCTOR *helps* IAN *with* TABON, *the robots are beginning to lose control of their movements, their arms are swinging more and more and they begin to move blindly about, like mad ants.* THE DERIVITRONS *meanwhile are still keeping up their chant.*)

              *6. A Corridor.*

              (BARBARA *and* SUSAN *race along the corridor.*)

              *7. The Laboratory.*

              (THE DOCTOR *and* IAN, *who is half-carrying, half-dragging* TABON, *back away from the robots and their wildly flailing arms.*)

THE DOCTOR:   Get back, get back. Let us out.

IAN:          Down, Doctor!

              (*They duck down and to one side as the robots surge past them. Two of the robots crash together, head on. They do this again and again until finally one of them manages to pass the other.* THE DOCTOR *and* IAN *continue to crouch down out of the way.*)

THE DOCTOR: They didn't see us. The robots are out of control. Look!

(THE PERFECT ONE *is pinned against a wall by a robot, who is repeatedly crashing into him.* IAN *races over and pulls* THE PERFECT ONE *away from danger.* THE DOCTOR *meanwhile has got* TABON *over to the doorway.*)

IAN: This way.

(IAN *pulls the semi-conscious body of* THE PERFECT ONE *towards the door.*)

Come on you. They can break you up after we've gone.

## 8. *A CORRIDOR.*

THE DOCTOR: Leave him here.

IAN: We can't. They'll be out of control everywhere. We can't ditch him until we get to the ship.

THE DOCTOR: Barbara and Susan! I forgot, there'll be creatures everywhere!

IAN: If you can manage him... come on.

(*They move off down the corridor,* THE DOCTOR *supporting* TABON, *and* IAN *half-dragging* THE PERFECT ONE.)

## 9. *THE DINING HALL.*

(SUSAN *and* BARBARA *are standing looking*

*through the window at the courtyard beyond. A robot, left there to guard the TARDIS, is there, his arms flailing wildly. The light on top of the police box is glowing.*)

SUSAN: The TARDIS is alive again. Barbara, she's alive!

BARBARA: But how do we get past that creature to get in?

SUSAN: We've got to think of a way.

### 10. A CORRIDOR.

(IAN *and* THE DOCTOR *are at the head of some stairs.* TABON *finally begins to recover consciousness.*)

TABON: What is happening? Where are you taking me?

THE DOCTOR: All your creatures, Derivitrons and robots, they're out of control.

TABON: He...?

IAN: I've got him. There was a robot trying to smash his head in. Don't stop to talk.

(*They move off down the stairs.*)

### 11. THE ATOMIC MAGAZINE.

(*The column of liquid is rising and falling very erratically in the tube.*)

*12. A CORRIDOR.*

(THE DOCTOR *and* TABON *come down some stairs.* THE DOCTOR *looks back in alarm, and goes up again to help* IAN.)

THE DOCTOR: Ian.

IAN: Take him. I've twisted my ankle. Easy. Easy. He weighs a ton!

(*Together they lower* THE PERFECT ONE *to the floor and prop him up against a wall.* TABON *puts his ear against* THE PERFECT ONE'*s head.*)

THE DOCTOR: How badly is he affected?

TABON: This state of unconsciousness is quite foreign to him.

IAN: How close is he to sending us all sky high?

TABON: That is what I am trying to hear.

IAN: Hear?

TABON: The personality centre of his brain... the cerebrum cortex is the liquified metal, Azzintium. In this liquid form it can store electrical and magnetic impulses almost to infinity, but its liquification range is within point six of a degree of temperature.

THE DOCTOR: Outside of which, either way, it solidifies?

TABON: Yes.

IAN: No more Perfect One. No more us.

TABON: If the power intake is not used up in movement and thought, the temperature will soon begin to rise. We will have to get him moving.

IAN: Have we got enough time to leave him here and make it to the ship?

THE DOCTOR: We don't know if we've enough there to get the TARDIS going.

TABON: Get him upright against the wall.

(IAN *and* THE DOCTOR *help him to raise* THE PERFECT ONE *up, until he is standing.* TABON *slaps his face.*)

IAN: No!

TABON: Creature of mine, you were made to move and speak. Move now. Speak now.

(*He slaps him again.*)

Move! Speak!

IAN: Maybe it's nearly solid now.

TABON: We would have heard a crackling noise.

(THE PERFECT ONE *mumbles drowsily.*)

PERFECT ONE: Live forever... Live... Live.

TABON: Take one arm each and pull him along. Make him walk.

(*As they start to move forward, an out of control robot comes at them.* IAN *shoulders it out of the way and they move off down the corridor.*)


*13. THE DINING HALL.*

(SUSAN *and* BARBARA *are still staring through the window at the* TARDIS *and the robot.*)

SUSAN:      But why is he swaying around like that?

BARBARA:    I know... The primitive ones have always been so
            stately and deliberate.

SUSAN:      He looks angry... you know, like a mad elephant.

BARBARA:    The robots... they've been affected, too. Like the
            Derivitrons with that chanting. Susan, if we go out
            there he won't even see us. He's all... he's got bees
            in his head.

SUSAN:      But he's right in front of the door.

BARBARA:    We won't get inside, standing here. We'll have to go
            up to him and see what he does do.

            (SUSAN *immediately runs out and* BARBARA *rushes
            after her.*)

            Together, Susan, together!


            *14. THE COURTYARD.*

            (SUSAN *and* BARBARA *approach the mad robot.*)

BARBARA:    I'll see if I can lead him off. You get the door open.

SUSAN:      Remember how fast they can move.

            (BARBARA *gets closer to the robot.*)

BARBARA:    Come and get me. Hey! Hey! Come and get me.

            (*The robot moves towards* BARBARA *and she
            quickly backs away.* SUSAN *dashes towards the
            TARDIS door. She is just about to put her key in
            the lock when the robot stops and turns.*)

            Come and...

*(The words die on her lips, as the robot swings round on* SUSAN.*)*

Susan... look out!

*(The robot grabs* SUSAN *and lifts her into the air. Across the courtyard,* IAN *comes into view. He hobbles across as fast as he can and rushes at the robot, who releases* SUSAN. IAN *swings the robot around and stops as* THE PERFECT ONe *stands in his way.)*

IAN:             Get him out of the way.

*(The robot, with a swipe of his arm, knocks* THE PERFECT ONE *aside and moves on out of view.* THE PERFECT ONE *lies motionless at the foot of the police box.* TABON *and* THE DOCTOR *move over to him. There is a thick black treacly substance oozing from the back of his head.* TABON *touches it.)*

TABON:           His skull has been split. It's the brain insulation.

THE DOCTOR:      Around the Azzintium?

TABON:           Yes. Get into your ship, Doctor... get away from here. I'll try and stop the flow... but it's under pressure. I can't do much.

THE DOCTOR:      But you, Tabon. We can take you back to Luxor.

TABON:           Listen.

*(They hear the crackling sound that* SUSAN *and* BARBARA *heard when they tripped* THE PERFECT ONE.*)*

This place is doomed.

THE DOCTOR:    We're not leaving you here.

TABON:    That atomic device we saw. It's enough to obliterate this whole planet.

(THE DOCTOR *tries to pull* TABON *away from* THE PERFECT ONE, *but* TABON *resists and continues to press his hands against its skull.*)

THE DOCTOR:    We are not leaving you here to die.

TABON:    Please, my friends. I chose sleep before because I was too much of a coward to face death. I'm stronger now.

SUSAN:    We can take you to Luxor.

TABON:    When they see this planet disappear out of the sky, perhaps they will learn something... and have you to thank for it. It's my life now, and my death. Go... you've no time to lose.

THE DOCTOR:    God keep you, Tabon.

(*He turns from* TABON *and one by one they go into the ship.*)


15. *THE TARDIS CONTROL ROOM.*

(THE DOCTOR *goes straight to the control console and sets the various controls in motion. The lights inside the TARDIS are not nearly as bright as usual and, although the central column starts to rise, it quickly shudders to a halt.*)

THE DOCTOR:    We're still underpowered. We'll have to wait. Susan, turn on the audio-scan.

(SUSAN *operates a control and on the screen* TABON *and* THE PERFECT ONE *appear. The crackling sound can be heard now, louder than before.*)

BARBARA: It's the same noise we heard when he went over our trip wire.

IAN: We were in the atomic magazine when that happened. Oh God, how long do we have to wait?

### 16. *THE ATOMIC MAGAZINE.*

(*The liquid level is steadily rising up the tube towards the danger mark.*)

### 17. *THE TARDIS CONTROL ROOM.*

(THE DOCTOR *steps back from the console.*)

THE DOCTOR: I've set us on a time course. We can't go up in the space dimension and risk the dome not opening.

SUSAN: TARDIS, TARDIS suck in the power. Take us away from this horrible place.

(THE DOCTOR *puts his arm round* SUSAN *and all four of the travellers look anxiously at the view screen.*)

BARBARA: How long have we got?

THE DOCTOR: I don't know. It's longer because of him.

IAN: We found him asleep in a coffin.

SUSAN: It's getting louder.

THE DOCTOR: The personality centre in his brain is solidifying. I suppose we have until the process is complete.

IAN: I'm glad I know that.

THE DOCTOR: How is your ankle?

IAN: Swollen. I hope it stays that way, at least for the next hour or so.

SUSAN: Have we got that long?

THE DOCTOR: No...

18. *THE ATOMIC MAGAZINE.*

(*The liquid level is now over three-quarters of the way up the tube.*)

19. *THE TARDIS CONTROL ROOM.*

(SUSAN *gazes anxiously at the central column.*)

SUSAN: Turn. Turn!

BARBARA: Is there any protection for us in here... if it doesn't turn?

(THE DOCTOR, *who is standing with* IAN *at another part of the control console, shakes his head. Then suddenly, he points at an indicator on the panel.*)

THE DOCTOR: See, it's beginning to gather strength.

BARBARA: So is that noise. I wish it would stop.

IAN: Hold on, Barbara. I bet Tabon feels the same way.

THE DOCTOR: Only until we are gone.

SUSAN:    Grandfather, when he put us in those terrible chairs I didn't care if I lived or died. I want to live now. We're all here in the TARDIS and I want us to live.


20. *THE ATOMIC CONTROL ROOM.*

(*The liquid reaches the danger mark.*)


21. *THE TARDIS CONTROL ROOM.*

(*The central column begins to move. The familiar sound of the TARDIS dematerialisation circuits gathers strength over the by now much louder crackling sound.*)

THE DOCTOR:    It's moving. We're away. It's moving.

SUSAN:    God, get us clear.

IAN:    Look at the screen.

(*As they begin to dematerialise, the view of the building on the screen becomes the lighted city, and then the whole planet. Suddenly the planet disappears in a great ball of flame and inside the TARDIS its occupants are thrown about. Gradually the shock waves die down and they realise to their relief that they are safe.*)

# AFTERWORD

In preparing Anthony Coburn's script of *The Masters of Luxor* for publication, a balance had to be struck between the separate and often quite different requirements of the casual reader and the avid fan. The purists amongst you would probably argue that not one comma, not one full stop, should be changed from the original script, but the more casual reader would very likely be confused and put off, for instance, by references to 'Suzanne' rather than the familiar 'Susan'. By listing the minor changes made below, we are hopefully satisfying the needs of both factions.

Had this story been given the go-ahead and actually reached production, these discrepancies would most certainly have been corrected in the final version of the script. Indeed, an important aspect of the series in its formative years was the consistency of the writing between separate stories and writers, due in large part to the diligence of the script-editor of the day, David Whitaker.

The following are the changes that were made:

* SUSAN is referred to throughout the original script as SUZANNE.
* The TARDIS is referred to by Susan and The Doctor as TARDIS - never "*the* TARDIS".
* Ian frequently calls The Doctor "Doc".
* The Doctor addresses Susan several times as "Sue", something which the onscreen Doctor never did.
* The Doctor addresses Ian by his first name, and on one occasion even calls him "son", rather than the more familiar "Chesterton" or "my boy".
* Ian repeatedly uses the word "yair" when he means yes. Whether this was meant as some form of dialect is not known, but since it is used several times, clearly was not just a spelling mistake.

In hindsight, other changes would also have been made, but whenever possible we have resisted the temptation to make alterations unless absolutely necessary. It is highly likely, for instance, that few, if any, of the mild blasphemies that appear throughout the script would have been left in or the discussion about God in episode six. Similarly, a number of Ian's and Susan's exclamations ("Holy Moley!") seem to belong more to a B-movie than to classic *Doctor Who*, but these are all presented as written in the original script. Note also that in episode two The Derivitron is given the name Proto. However, for subsequent episodes Derivitrons are not specifically named. This is as written in the original script.

Another point of interest that differs from the accepted history of early *Doctor Who* is several specific references to the fact that Ian and Barbara are from Earth and that The Doctor and Susan are not ("you Earth people"), which ties in more with the pilot episode than with the actually transmitted version of *An Unearthly Child*.

The concept of the TARDIS being able to hover, like a helicopter, is also novel and, given the limited special effects resources of 1963, it is difficult to imagine how such scenes would have been convincingly realised. Similarly, the scene where the TARDIS is pulled into the open 'petals' of the building would have been difficult to achieve on the show's limited budget.

A nice touch is Ian's reference to "the projectionist has gone home". Even though he has experienced for himself the perils of the stone-age in *The Tribe of Gum*, one part of his mind is still telling him that the whole thing is still just a trick. A far cry from the companions of today, who enter the TARDIS, utter the obligatory "wow, it's so big!", and then happily accept everything that is thrown at them.

Note also, that the idea of the recap of the previous episode's cliffhanger, which was to become one of the golden rules of *Doctor Who*, does not feature in the script. However, the alternative 'sometime later' is used, for instance between the end of episode one and the beginning of episode two.

In reading the script, one should remember that the story was intended to be used instead of *The Daleks*. Given that, one cannot help but notice a number of similarities between the two stories and speculate as to the reasons for this. Did either writer see the other's script? Or, more likely, were these ideas also the work of David Whitaker? Certainly in more recent times it has not been uncommon for the script editor to come up with an idea, which an appointed script writer has then developed.

The building itself is very similar to the Dalek city on Skaro, with its many levels, its lifts and its windows looking out onto the dead planet, although the planet itself is perhaps more reminiscent of Vortis in *The Web Planet*.

The Fault Locator, as described by Anthony Coburn, is exactly the same as that used in *The Daleks*, when The Doctor uses it as an excuse to visit the city. Note, however, in this story that The Doctor is apparently quite willing to leave and that it is Susan who initially wants to manoeuvre the TARDIS closer to the building. Barbara, however, is written perfectly true to her 'real' character and is the one that senses evil. In hindsight, perhaps the others should have listened to Barbara, as she was of course invariably right!

In episode four, the concept of getting into the building through the mountains is again virtually identical to *The Daleks*, although in the latter story this is a more significant part of the action than in *The Masters of Luxor*.

Anthony Coburn's script ends somewhat abruptly, with The Doctor and his companions safely back in the TARDIS. Given that this story would have been shown instead of *The Daleks*, we did consider adding the final brief scene from that story which leads into *Edge of Destruction*, in which there is an explosion aboard the TARDIS, the four travellers are thrown to the floor and all the lights go out. Since it is known that the two-part *Edge of Destruction* was hastily written to fill a gap that had appeared due to problems with scheduling of future stories, had *The Masters of Luxor* been produced, it is quite possible that *Edge of Destruction* would not have even been written. We therefore decided against adding this scene.

Anthony ended his script with the words 'And I would rather leave the rest of this until I can link it properly to the opening scene of the next episode'. Perhaps that is the best way to end it.

DOCTOR WHO

THE SCRIPTS

# THE DAEMONS
## BY ROBERT SLOMAN
## AND BARRY LETTS

An ancient archaeological barrow. A White Witch warning
of impending doom. A trio of formidable foes - Azal,
Boc and ... The Master! The Doctor and Jo Grant, his
assistant, are soon to come face-to-face with an evil
almost as old as time itself.

Read the complete, classic script of a story voted by fans
the best ever Doctor Who, together with fascinating
background and technical information.

For a complete list of Titan's Doctor Who publications,
please send a large SAE to Titan Books Mail Order,
19 Valentine Place, London SE1 8QH.
Please quote reference DW1.